Kate Furbish
and the Flora of Maine

Kate Furbish
and the
Flora of Maine

Ada Graham
and
Frank Graham, Jr.

Tilbury House, Publishers
Gardiner, Maine

Tilbury House, Publishers
132 Water Street
Gardiner, Maine 04345
Copyright © 1995 by Ada Graham and Frank Graham, Jr.
Copyright © Furbish watercolors and drawings by the President and Trustees of Bowdoin College.
Copyright © black and white photographs of the watercolors and drawings by John McKee.
Color photographs copyright © by Tilbury House, Publishers.

Library of Congress Cataloging-in-Publication Data:

Graham, Ada. Kate Furbish and the flora of Maine / by Ada Graham and Frank Graham, Jr.
            p.   cm.
    Includes bibliographical references (P.   ) and index.
    ISBN 0-88448-175-1. -- ISBN 0-88448-176-X (pbk.)
    1. Furbish, Kate. 2. Botanical artists--Maine--Biography. 3. Botanical illustration--Maine.
I. Graham, Frank, 1925- II. Title
QK98. 183.F87G73 1995
581' .022'2--dc20   [B]   94-45680
                                                                               CIP

Text and cover designed by Edith Allard
Editing and Production: Mark Melnicove, Jennifer Elliott, Lisa Reece, and Devon Phillips
Color photography and color separations: Graphic Color, Waterville, Maine
Printing (text): The Stinehour Press, Lunenburg, Vermont
Printing (jackets and covers): The John Pow Company, South Boston, Massachusetts
Binding: Horowitz-Rae, Fairfield, New Jersey

10 9 8 7 6 5 4 3 2 1

Contents

Illustrations

Kate Furbish's original paintings and drawings have been photographed in black and white for publication by John McKee. The historic black and white photographs are courtesy of Bowdoin College. The color photography is by Graphic Color, Waterville, Maine.

Acknowledgments

The work and details of Kate Furbish's life survive because of the many people who believe that the private past is important. To those people, and the institutions they represent, we express our gratitude.

The Bowdoin College Library in Brunswick, Maine, has served as the faithful guardian of the Furbish sketches and paintings since 1908. We are indebted to The President and Trustees of the College for access to those works and for permission to reproduce them.

We thank Sherrie S. Bergman, Bowdoin College Librarian; her predecessor, Arthur Monke; and Dianne M. Gutscher, Curator of Special Collections, for their unremitting interest and assistance in seeing this book through to publication. We also thank Richard A. Mersereau, Executive Assistant to the President and Governing Boards of Bowdoin College, and Lucie G. Teegarden, Director of Publications, for listening to our plans and patiently answering our many questions.

Lenore M. Dickinson, Librarian of the Gray Herbarium of Harvard University, and her staff made available to us the extensive correspondence of Kate Furbish with leading botanists of her time. In particular, we would like to thank Dr. Elizabeth A. Shaw, Bibliographer at the Herbarium, for help in finding specific letters and references of extreme importance to our work. Permission to quote from these materials was granted by The Gray Herbarium Library, Archives, Harvard University, Cambridge, Massachusetts.

We could not even have begun our work without the enthusiastic cooperation of Kate Furbish's grandniece, Alice Furbish Kerr of Bloomfield, Connecticut. The late Anne Streeter Decius and the late Joyce Streeter Freedman made available to us journals and other Furbish family materials essential for the completion of our work.

The Josselyn Botanical Society of Maine has passed down to our time not only details of Kate Furbish's botanical collecting but also the spirit in which she explored the "Garden of Maine" (to use Merritt Fernald's phrase). Charles D. Richards, Professor of Botany Emeritus, University of Maine, and a former president of the society, has been extremely generous with his knowledge and advice in helping us to complete our book. Other Josselyn members who have provided helpful information are L.M. Eastman, another former president of the society; the society's current president, Sally Rooney; its treasurer, Marilyn Dwelley; Susan C. Gawler, chief "biographer" of the Furbish's lousewort; Alison Dibble; Eleanor Hall; Candy McKellar; and Harry R. Tyler, Jr., of the Critical Areas Program of the Maine State Planning Office.

Our debt to Judith Falk is made clear at the end of our story.

Ada Graham
Frank Graham, Jr.
Milbridge, Maine

Foreword

During the late 1970s the name Kate Furbish — or, more exactly, a plant named for her, the Furbish's lousewort — became a rallying cry for environmentalists all across the United States. Both the woman and the plant were unlikely catalysts to produce a change in the public's attitude toward the preservation of endangered species.

Kate Furbish, painter and amateur botanist, first brought to public attention the plant that bears her name when she discovered it in 1880 in what was then a sparsely settled and remote region of Maine along the Saint John River. The Furbish's lousewort, a wild snapdragon, is not known from any place in the world other than the banks of this river. Botanists soon realized that it was rare even there. It was found again periodically along the Saint John; botanists collected the plant at Fort Kent in 1946, but for 30 years afterward there was no record of it. Finally, the Smithsonian Institution, in its Report of Endangered and Threatened Plant Species of the United States (1975), listed the Furbish's lousewort as "probably extinct."

During the summer of 1976, I was engaged by the U.S. Army Corps of Engineers to survey the upper Saint John River for rare and endangered plants. The survey report was part of an Environmental Impact Statement that the Corps was preparing for the proposed $670 million Dickey-Lincoln hydroelectric power plant, which was to be built on the Saint John in the towns of Allagash and Saint Francis. Behind the dam, which was to be larger than Egypt's Aswan Dam, 88,000 acres of riverbank and forest would be submerged.

Before starting the survey, I drew up a list of rare plants occurring in northern Maine that could be endangered if the power plant were built — plants that I definitely wanted to look for in connection with the survey. Furbish's lousewort was one of these plants, because I was not convinced that it was extinct.

I arrived in the town of Allagash on the afternoon of June 27, 1976, to begin my survey. After settling into my cabin and having dinner, I took a stroll along the river to see what I could find before dark. Not more than 50 feet from the spot where I descended the riverbank, I came across a colony of Furbish's lousewort. It was not yet in flower, but a flowering stalk was beginning to push upward from the fernlike basal leaves. It would be another month before the colony would fully bloom.

Walking along the riverbank for a distance of a half-mile, I encountered about six more plants. Furbish's lousewort was definitely not extinct. These specimens were in the area that would be flooded if the Dickey-Lincoln dam project were built. How abundant were the plants, and did they occur outside the area to be impounded by the proposed dam?

In my survey, I failed to find the Furbish's lousewort upriver from the town of Allagash, so I decided to search further in the town itself. This proved very fruitful: I found a considerable number of plants along the river in town in addition to the ones I had discovered on my first evening. All these plants, with the exception of one, were growing on the south bank of the river, where they received shade for a good part of the day.

In the fall of 1976, word of the rediscovery of Furbish's lousewort reached the press, and newspapers across the country carried colorful articles about the plant that could halt construction of the huge hydroelectric project. The Endangered Species Act of 1973 required interagency consultation to keep federal projects from arbitrarily disrupting the habitat of endangered species. The Office of Rare and Endangered Species in Washington, D.C., drafted a petition to list the Furbish's lousewort as endangered and in need of protection. Then, if Congress funded the project and construction began, any environmental group could sue the Army Corps of Engineers for violating the law.

A great uproar followed. Proponents of the dam argued that it would supply the Northeast with abundant cheap power and provide jobs and money to an economically depressed part of Maine. Conservationists argued that it would flood some 88,000 acres of wilderness and destroy one of the nation's truly wild rivers. It could lead to the extinction of certain rare species of plants or animals, including the Furbish's lousewort.

The lousewort received widespread publicity. The conjunction of the names Furbish and lousewort was too much for the sloganeers and headline writers to resist. Bumper stickers and T-shirts branded the names on the public consciousness as a symbol of the struggle against the dam builders. Articles appeared in newspapers and magazines about the woman who had collected the plant that might derail the multimillion-dollar project.

On surveys the following year I discovered five localities of the lousewort along the Saint John River downstream from the location of the proposed dam. I was especially pleased to find specimens at Van Buren, which may be where Kate Furbish first found the rare plant. In theory, then, the dam would not necessarily flood out the world's last Furbish's lousewort.

On the other hand, the area downriver from Fort Kent has changed considerably since the time when Kate Furbish explored it. Houses and potato fields now dominate where spruce and fir once lined the banks. In Van Buren and elsewhere the water level has risen due to a dam built at Grand Falls, New Brunswick. The few remaining lousewort habitats downstream from Fort Kent are located so precariously that any alteration of the habitat might wipe them out permanently and threaten the very existence of Furbish's lousewort in the Saint John River valley.

There is doubt that the dam will ever be built, at least on a massive scale. But the uproar was beneficial in that it helped to bring before the public the ethical question of whether human beings have the right to condemn any species to extinction.

There was another benefit to the controversy over Furbish's lousewort. It called attention to a remarkable woman and her work. I first heard of Kate Furbish in 1953, when I attended a field meeting of the Josselyn Botanical Society, which I later served as president for more than a decade. Some of the members at that meeting had known Kate Furbish and had botanized with her during earlier meetings. Clarence Knowlton, a long-time member of the society, had served as treasurer when Miss Furbish was president in 1912. Ralph Bean, an ardent botanist who collected plants extensively throughout Maine, spoke fondly of Kate Furbish as a small, energetic woman with keen powers of observation and the ability to outlast many of the younger members in the field.

Finally, the controversy shed light on the importance of the amateur botanist. Kate Furbish and many other devoted amateurs have contributed enormously to our knowledge of plant life. Because of the long hours they have put in, exploring remote areas and collecting plant specimens, we now have fairly good records of the occurrence and distribution of plants in Maine.

But that is all part of the story that will be told in the following pages.

Charles D. Richards
Professor of Botany Emeritus
University of Maine

Preface

This is the first publication of a representative collection of the drawings and watercolors made by Kate Furbish. The text that accompanies it describes the life and times of a nineteenth-century amateur botanist.

In contrast to the lives of other Victorian women who have caught the attention of modern readers, that of Kate Furbish was not one of marked privilege or broad social symbolism. Her story belongs, in a sense, to what has been called "the literature of private life."

But the physical and social environments in which Kate Furbish created an identity for herself play a large role in that story. The landscape of Maine, with its varied flora, attracted and ultimately absorbed her attention. Her long life, spanning nearly a century, coincided with the development of botany as a prestigious science in the United States. Meanwhile, her almost continuous moving about from one place to another during most of her maturity prompted her to leave a record in letters and journals — details of family life, religious reflections, opinions on society and the arts, incidents of travel, and botanical shoptalk.

Kate Furbish took life seriously. She filled it with substance — exercising imagination, judgment, and persistence — supported by the conviction that what she made of her life mattered.

Creating this book was an adventure. Living relatives of Kate Furbish were the first people we approached about possible leads concerning the details of her life and character. Once convinced that the project was desirable, these family members volunteered diaries and family letters that had not been available to researchers before.

The notes in the diaries suggested further sources: the Gray Herbarium at Harvard University in Cambridge, Massachusetts, the Portland Society of Natural History, and distant relatives. Soon, with the individual labels of the paintings and drawings in the 14 folios — the Flora of Maine — presented by Kate Furbish to Bowdoin College, and the letters and papers that were emerging, the authors found it possible to piece together an explicit picture of how the botanist-artist set about establishing the goal of the Flora for herself and how she executed the task.

Rather than simply writing an essay to accompany visual material, we found ourselves in the agreeable situation of following Kate Furbish's footsteps over the face of Maine. Assistance came in the form of publications of the Maine Critical Areas Program, which helped us find the stands of plants, or "stations," that Kate Furbish herself collected from and painted.

As we studied Kate Furbish in the context of the social and cultural life of nineteenth-century Brunswick, examining her work within the New England circle of amateur and professional field botanists, illustrations and text began to blend together. Although the paintings were chosen on the basis of geographic distribution, physical habitats, plant families, and visual appeal (variety, size, rhythm, and degree of execution) before much of the text material was uncovered, there was no problem matching them to the developing story. The methodical development of the original Flora dovetailed with the description of the woman's life and times. The result was a continuous flow of floral images accompanied by text that confirms and enhances the visual experience by narrative and historical perspective.

We believe that these color and black-and-white illustrations reflect the work of Kate Furbish as completely as possible. Difficult choices had to be made. When there were duplicate renderings of the same plant, or renderings of closely related species, we had two considerations: which was the most typical in botanical terms, and which the most artful to our twentieth-century sensibilities?

Many of Kate Furbish's illustrations appear unfinished to us. That is, the coloring that would please us is missing. Yet for her purpose — comparing the plant in hand against the typically realized pictorial analysis —

they are indeed finished. There is never any difficulty in comprehending the nature of the complete plant. (This is not the same, however, as a scheme for recognition, such as one would find in a guidebook.) Nevertheless, we chose the paintings that were, on the whole, most complete.

Kate Furbish had a strong interest in the "individual plant." She frequently alluded to individual plants, and commented on their characteristics. She did not seek to convey some general notion of the species. She felt a plant's living posture as it responded to the encouragements and vicissitudes of life — sun, wind, soil, moisture, crowding — in a word, how it grew and mastered its fate. In our opinion and that of many others, her interest in the individual gave her work its unique character. It was this particular quality that we sought to convey by careful selection.

Kate Furbish's Flora communicates strongly across a century and will continue to do so to all who have an interest in, and a feeling for, growing things.

Maine

MAINE SCENICS

Autumn on the Maine Coast.

Photo © David Ransaw

MS 764 A

MAINE SCENE Inc. - Box 580- UNION MAINE 04862
☎ 207-785-4502

Printed in Italy
by Litovald

Kate Furbish
and the Flora of Maine

BLUETS (Houstonia caerulea)

Kate Furbish painted all the known flora of Maine, each from a specific plant found at a particular location.
This is one of the spring wildflowers she saw on childhood walks around Brunswick with her father.

The Brunswick Background

Benjamin and Mary Lane Furbish and their first child, Catherine, moved from Exeter, New Hampshire, to Brunswick, on the coast of Maine in 1835. Catherine, or Kate as she was known almost from the beginning, had been born in Exeter the previous year. Yet during a peripatetic life that would span nearly a century, and during which she would forge a reputation as a field botanist and unrivaled painter of Maine's extensive flora, it was always to Brunswick that she would return.

This town of nearly 4,000 people had a distinctive air of industry and cultural ferment. Indeed, Henry Wadsworth Longfellow held the chair of modern languages at Brunswick's Bowdoin College, though he relinquished it that year, 1835, to accept a similar post at Harvard College. The historians George Augustus Wheeler and Henry Warren Wheeler have described Brunswick as it was a few months after the arrival of the Furbishes:

In 1836, Brunswick Village contained the colleges, the cotton and woolen factories, nearly four hundred dwellings, forty stores, three printing offices, two banks, two hotels, one iron foundry, two machine-shops, two flour-mills, and twenty saw-mills. Seven stages arrived and departed daily, and often three or four extra ones.

Furbish ancestors have been traced to northern New England in the middle of the seventeenth century. Old records show that William Furbish was granted land in Dover, New Hampshire, in 1648. He was a taxpayer there in 1659; five years later he owned land in Kittery, Maine. One of his grandsons, John Furbish, lived at South Berwick, Maine, and several of his descendants married women from the nearby town of Wells. Samuel Furbish, a seafaring man and later a farmer, and his wife, Abigail Davis of Wells, had seven children, one of whom, Benjamin, was born in Wells in 1807.

As a young man, Benjamin was apprenticed to a craftsman in tin plate and sheet iron. He spent three years learning the trade and later worked for a tinsmith in Saint Andrews, New Brunswick. After eighteen months he returned to New England, married Mary Lane, and with a partner set up his first tin-plate business in Exeter, New Hampshire. It was from Exeter that the young family moved to Brunswick.

Though always in poor health after an early case of rheumatic fever, Benjamin Furbish was active in business and community projects for most of his life. A contemporary description provides a picture of a strong personality, many aspects of which he passed on to his only daughter.

He was reserved, uncommunicative at times, but

CRANESBILL (Geranium bicknellii)
*When the petals fall from the flower, the erect pistil,
thought to resemble a crane's bill, remains.*

still, beneath all this reserve, there flowed a vein of humor which rendered him a most desirable companion in social life, and which was the charm of home. He was keen in his criticisms, but no ill nature worked them. A man with a clear judgment, enlarged and liberal views of men and things, reading much, he proved an excellent citizen, ready to promote any good object, with labor or purse; and his fellow-citizens marked their appreciation of the merits of the man by repeatedly electing him to fill offices of honor and trust in his home for many years.

The tin-plate shop that Benjamin Furbish established in Brunswick soon expanded into a successful hardware store, where he sold mowing machines, wheel rakes, fruit trees, and tomato plants "of my own raising." Furbish was something of an inventor, and developed cooking stoves as well as an early airtight stove. He became one of the leading tradesmen in a community that was beginning to take advantage of the industry made possible by the turbulent Androscoggin River, which flows past the town toward Merrymeeting Bay, a few miles away. The town's historians, scarcely concealing communal pride, describe this resource as it was in the nineteenth century:

Where the banks of the river approach each other and the compressed waters go rolling on between the firm bounds of rock, the scene begins to change. Here is the beginning of the notable Brunswick Falls, the finest water-power on the Atlantic coast.... Its numerous cascades afford not only varied and picturesque views, but furnish a motive-power unsurpassed in New England within so small a space.

Three years after arriving in Brunswick, Benjamin Furbish built a large white frame house for his growing family on O'Brien (later Cumberland) Street, which had fewer than a half-dozen dwellings but was soon to become a major residential street.

Five sons were born into the family; two died in infancy. The survivors were John, Edward, and Frank, and for a time they and young Catherine formed a close-knit Victorian family. There is no evidence that Catherine was dominated to her detriment by her out-

SHADBUSH (Amelanchier canadensis)
Shadbush is among the earliest of the white-flowering shrubs to bloom in Maine.

spoken father and ambitious brothers. Rather, she seems to have absorbed much of her father's business acumen and an interest in the technological developments of the day. On walks with her father around town she first learned the names of common plants.

There were additional influences on Catherine. She grew up during the period of Maine's most accelerated development. Brunswick played a special, sometimes atypical, role in that development. Maine had been only an outlying district of Massachusetts until 1820, when it was granted statehood as part of the Missouri Compromise. Spurred by its variety of small industries, Brunswick began to flex political mus-

WILD VIOLET (Viola pllens)
This tiny species, with round or heart-shaped leaves, sends up its delicate white blossoms on slender stems.

be the equal of any in the state. Benjamin Furbish took an active part in various school committees. Brunswick had a number of private schools, or seminaries. Young Catherine Furbish attended the school operated by Deborah Folsom. Her father paid a bill for her schooling from December 30, 1844, to April 19, 1845, which amounted to three dollars, plus an extra dollar for a course in Latin.

Brunswick already had an active cultural life. The first theatrical event in its history had occurred in 1828, when a company of comedians from the Tremont Theater in Boston performed such contemporary hits as *The Honeymoon* and *The Young Widow.* Concerts, too, were given, but

cles. The town fathers had seen to it that the first college in the state was opened in Brunswick in 1802, with both money and a name from the family of James Bowdoin, a prominent commercial and political leader of the Revolutionary War era from Massachusetts. With statehood, ambitious Brunswick citizens again proved influential. They persuaded the first state legislature to establish the Maine Medical School in 1821, and it remained part of Bowdoin College until 1921.

The college was simply the tip of Brunswick's educational apparatus. While men like Henry Wadsworth Longfellow and future United States president Franklin Pierce were matriculating at Bowdoin, the local residents developed a public school system that was said to

the most frequent, well-attended cultural events were public lectures. Given singly or in series, they covered a variety of topics reflecting the interests of the day: English grammar, electricity, vegetable life, storms and meteorology (delivered by an eloquent professor who was widely known as "The Storm King"), hygiene, and explosions of steam boilers. In the aftermath of a series of lectures on vegetarianism, local butchers nearly went into bankruptcy. The audiences, in fact, seemed to carry open minds with them to lecture halls, for Brunswick's historians wrote, "In 1826 John Cleaves Symmes, a believer in an interior world, access to which was open to voyagers in the southern hemisphere, gave a course of three lectures, which was well attended, and commanded

LARGER BLUE FLAG (Iris versicolor)
This species, fond of marshes and wet meadows,
is similar to our garden iris.

EVENING PRIMROSE (Oenothera cruciata)
Its flowers, with the prominent cross-shaped stigma, open toward evening.

respect and interest, as Mr. Symmes was not considered a charlatan, however erroneous might be his theory."

Brunswick was a church-going community. Benjamin Furbish gave his allegiance to the Congregationalists, a denomination challenged only by the Free Baptists as having the most members among the town's Protestant churches But the 1820s and 1830s were a period of unbridled enthusiasm for reform in the United States, with most of the uproar focused on temperance and abolition. No community in the country played a larger part in these movements than the little town of Brunswick.

The first organized assault on the demon rum in Maine may have been made in Brunswick in 1813, when the Brunswick, Topsham, and Harpswell Society for the Suppression of Intemperance was formed. There was not enough interest around the district, however, to sustain the movement. But the state, with a large number of single men living in the comparative isolation of fishing vessels and logging camps (where a ration of spirits was often the single remedy for all physical and psychological ills), was especially vulnerable to the evils of alcoholism. Agitation for prohibition grew in intensity until 1851, when Maine became the first state in the Union to ban the sale of liquor. The "Maine Law" became the model on which other states based their prohibition legislation.

POISON IVY (Toxicodendron radicans)
This poisonous variety of the sumac family is found throughout Maine, and the young Kate was surely aware of the old adage, "Leaves three, then flee; berries white, take flight."

Brunswick played an even more vital role in the other great issue of the day. Bowdoin College was a center of activity for the abolition of slavery. Professors at Bowdoin helped organize meetings to publicize the abolition movement and petition the federal government to relax the Fugitive Slave Law and other pro-slavery legislation.

Although abolitionist sentiment was abroad in Brunswick, there was no passion for equal rights. In the early days some residents had been slaveholders themselves, and a section of town voted to set off the resident blacks in a school district of their own and decreed that white children attend classes in summer and winter, and black children only in spring and autumn. Understandably, the Bowdoin professors lacked the support of all the townspeople in their fight for abolition. It was Harriet Beecher Stowe, the wife of a Bowdoin professor, who struck the greatest blow of all against slavery by writing *Uncle Tom's Cabin* in Brunswick.

Social and cultural ideas were in the air in Brunswick, mingling with the heady optimism of expanding commercial activity, and this climate surely touched Kate Furbish as she grew toward womanhood. Yet another reality held far greater fascination for her. In their history of the town, Wheeler and Wheeler described a hill locally called Mount Ararat, which lay on the other side of the Androscoggin River,

WILD STRAWBERRY (Fragaria virginiana)
The plant has been painted in fruit, while in the lower corner there is a detail of fruit with seeds.

QUEEN ANNE'S LACE (Daucus carota)
The plant's alternate name, wild carrot, refers to its edible root.

COMMON CINQUEFOIL (Potentilla simplex)
One of the many kinds of "five-finger" in Maine. This one, with yellow flowers, is
sometimes mistaken for the buttercup, but the cinquefoil's petals are not as shiny.

beyond Topsham, and which the people of Brunswick sometimes climbed on leisurely afternoons.

Upon the summit of this hill once stood a very respectable observatory rising higher than the surrounding trees. From the top of this observatory, or from the summit of one of the tallest trees, could be seen in one direction the Cathance River, winding like a silver thread through the evergreen foliage; in another direction, the bright waters of Merrymeeting Bay; farther still gleamed the broad line of the New Meadows River and the wide expanse of Casco Bay, the latter dotted with islands and swept by the white sails of vessels of every size. At the West, about sixty miles distant, the White Hills of New Hampshire are distinctly visible on clear days, while a glass reveals the observatory and church spires at Portland.

Perhaps it seemed like only a step to reach out from that view of a largely unspoiled landscape to the rest of the state and to discover and make known to the world Maine's marvelous variety of wild flowering plants.

PINK LADY'S SLIPPER (Cypripedium acaule)
This dramatic orchid, often looked for by botanists and other lovers of wild plants, grows well over a foot tall.
It is also called the moccasin flower.

A Victorian Outlook

"*I* think it probable that you are expecting a letter from me soon, and so, inclination prompting, I will write to you this dull dreary day."

So wrote Kate Furbish from Brunswick on October 13, 1861, to her "Dear cousin Pamela" in Wells, Maine. Twenty-seven-year-old Kate, living with her parents in the family home on O'Brien Street, had recently visited her Furbish cousins in Wells and was responding with her customary elaborate courtesy. But in this and other letters to Pamela Furbish, she expressed herself with a lightness and candor she never showed again, revealing the curious blend of Victorian convention and unrelenting personal quest that lifted her outside her restricted family and community circle.

After complimenting Pamela, she extended her embrace to all Furbishes, far and wide. "I am very fond of my relatives, anyone bearing my Father's name interests me.... I am quite an antiquarian in my taste.... If 'twas the custom to live in clans, I should be a strong adherent to its customs. I admire to see relatives herded together and united in sentiment and feeling."

Although all members of the Furbish clan interested her, the one member she singled out for special attention was her cousin Oliver, whom she had seen again in Wells. "I wish I could see him every day for a year, so that I might learn him thoroughly. I would like to know him well enough to form a just estimate of his character. I know he is good hearted and quick to feel. I like him — I think he is very observing and notices all one's ways, and forms his opinion of a person from their ways."

Kate Furbish could have been writing about herself, for she too was often quick to feel and eager to learn everything thoroughly. Furthermore, her curiosity extended to herself. "I should think a good deal of his honest opinion of anyone, and have often thought when I have been with him that I'd give more for his honest opinion of me than for that of any other man I ever saw."

Apparently this was too strong even for a fervent admirer of all Furbishes, because she hastened to pull back. "Pardon this strain, Pamela, my thoughts ran away with me, I did not intend to write so much about him." And she went on to state her interest in other terms. "But before I drop him, I wish to beg you to reprove him for every wicked word he uses, do it gently, and I believe he will thank you for it. I don't think he wants to sin."

That apparent afterthought led directly to one of the most important concerns she shared with Pamela, the

JACK-IN-THE-PULPIT (Arisaema atrorubens)
"I have sketched with great care the plant on this sheet and find it quite different
from the ordinary," Kate Furbish noted of this specimen taken in Wells.
All the northeastern "Jacks" are thought to be one species.

nature and state of their immortal souls. "I am happy in the thought dear Pamela that I am opening a correspondence with a professing Christian, for we shall never be drained for matter to fill a friendly sheet."

Outside the circle of Furbishes, Kate found herself at this time most at home among Episcopalians, a group that barely outnumbered the Furbishes in Brunswick. (A survey a dozen years later uncovered only fifty-six members in the local Episcopalian congregation.) The nature of their liturgy touched the young woman's imagination. She wrote to her cousin: "To-day is Sunday. I have been at church all day — after being away from the Episcopal Church eight Sundays — its pure Liturgy seemed good to me, I can assure you. I am a great admirer of its service. 'Twas a happy day to my Soul when I found myself within its pale."

Earlier in 1861 her brother John had started a journal in which he concentrated mainly on business dealings and public affairs. It reflected the family's dependence on the stove (which he invariably wrote with a capital S) business. Beginning on March 15, the traffic in these items absorbed much of his attention. "We sold a Franklin Stove for $6.00 rather than store it all summer.... sold old cooking Stove on time, finished repairing an old Plymouth Rock Stove.... was sent a 'sample Stove' made to imitate the 'Stewart' in some respects. I despise all imitations and patronize them but little.... sold an old cook Stove which I had been able to fix up.

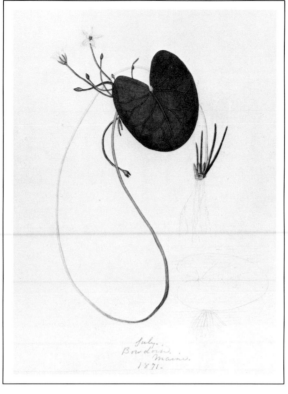

FLOATING HEART (Nymphoides cordata)
The leaves resemble those of water lilies, though the species is a member of the gentian family. It is a familiar plant of Maine's ponds.

At a small advance we are able to exchange with poor people and to give them a better Stove.... sold an Air Tight Stove today to go out to Jacksonville, Florida, for the wife of Maj. Stowe of the U.S. Army."

Sometimes the transactions led to wider reflections. "Went up to Mrs. Eph. Wall's and got a lot of [trunks] in which they take goods to Massachusetts. Thus we are a little benefited by a person's leaving town, though they have always been our customers. We cannot affard [sic] to loose [sic] any of our citizens. The town is really decreasing in population. One disadvantage in having a college in the place is its influence on society, driving out the lower and middle classes to places where they find themselves the equals of those about them."

John Furbish's journal from the spring of 1861 bristles with comments, both patriotic and pessimistic, about the Civil War. "War! War! Civil War!!" he exclaimed on Saturday, April 13. "A shudder passes over us when we think of such a thing. But it has already begun.... Nothing is thought or talked about now but our national troubles. The people are fast becoming as one man at the North and the 'Union' is the cry from all mouths." His patriotic fervor momentarily flickered in the rush of business worries, but soon steadied itself. "Trade may ccasc. Commerce be swept from the seas. But *'liberty'* must live!"

John Furbish was a loyal Republican, supporting his party and its leaders. Although he expressed his approval of President Lincoln's inaugural address, he

CANADA LILY (Lilium canadense)
*Despite the artist's relentless pursuit of botanical accuracy, here she also expressed
her pure joy in the contemplation of the Canada Lily's wild beauty.*

COMMON MILKWEED (Asclepias syriaca)
A common species of Maine's roadsides, it exudes a thick milky juice when broken.

felt a deeper satisfaction that a Maine man, Hannibal Hamlin, was the country's Vice President. On May 9, the native son came to town, and Furbish wrote, "Vice-President Hamlin passed through here today and it certainly gave me a new idea of the simplicity of our form of government: the next to the highest officer of our land passing from place to place as a citizen, none to herald or wait upon him."

In those days Maine citizens went to the polls in September. (Generally voting Republican in a Republican era, they gave rise to the saying "As Maine goes, so goes the nation.") On September 9, 1861, state elections were held, and Benjamin Furbish was elected to the legislature from Brunswick. Kate accompanied her father to Augusta for at least a part of that legislative session and was eager to write her cousin Pamela (by now usually addressed as "Millie") about her experiences in the state capital. "I have been away of late 'Millie'; I had a fine time, was at Augusta with Father three weeks, visited all the places of interest in the City. 'Twas pleasant visiting the State-House occasionally — as often generally there was smart speaking.... The Cavalry parades were fine, surpassing anything which I had conceived."

She may have been swept up momentarily in the pomp and circumstance of war, but she wrote to her cousin mainly of its darker side. "The Hospitals particularly drew upon my sympathies. How would your heart ache my dear 'Millie,' if you should go into a hall where there were 134 men stretched on beds of suffer-

WHITE ASH (Fraxinus americana)
*The green flowers that bloom in late May
in Maine forests are without petals.*

ing, and away from their homes. Too much cannot be done for the soldiers. I grudge no time which I spend for them."

The time that Kate Furbish did not grudge was spent, as it was by countless other women of the day, in making lint for bandages. "We pull out linen and lay it in layers evenly. All has been sent to St. Louis which has been made here.... My heart aches as day after day passes and we do not even see the beginning of the end [of this war]. One after another of my old friends enlist, are wounded or killed, and many yet live in honor to our Land."

At times she imagined herself bringing aid and sympathy to the soldiers in the thick of battle. Yet, like so many contemporary women who were afflicted with real or imagined weaknesses, she was unable to follow her imagination beyond the circle of her family. "I would I were a strong rugged woman. B. [Brunswick] would not hold me long I assure you. One of our B. girls is at Virginia and has the care of 100 wounded men — I wish I was with her, so many need more than one person. But 'tis useless the Surgeons would not pass me, let me beg ever so earnestly."

The mysterious weakness that seems to have been a Furbish legacy did not diminish her interest in Brunswick's dwindling male population. A man named Wilson, who went there to teach and was apparently an acquaintance of her cousin Oliver's, figured ocasionally in her correspondence. "'So you've seen Mr.

SMOOTH ROSE (Rosa blanda)
*One of the more benign roses, usually free of thorns in the upper stems,
with pale pink flowers. A plant of Maine's rocky slopes.*

W.,' I hear you ask? Yes 'Millie,' as large as life, but not as natural. I should not have thought of him had I [not] met him in the street, he is all *be-whiskered,* and that cunning little mouth is *all* covered up, and instead of being quiet and silent, he is lively and very sociable; at least the afternoon he called on me he was. I liked him."

There were some other pastimes in wartime Brunswick. Kate Furbish asked her cousin what she was reading and volunteered that she herself was reading a memoir, as well as *Don Quixote,* which she had never read in her youth. And in the especially somber moods that Maine's summer weather can occasionally induce, she turned to investigating the state of her soul. "Well, Millie, this is a cold rainy day, it seems little like

the middle of July as we picture it in our minds before it comes. I have been to Ch. [Church] all day and to S. [School] Oh! Millie: I feel tonight that I would no longer live in the poor dying state but would live nearer unto Christ. How hard it is with the temptations of the gay world pressing us on every side."

What terrors of the soul or flesh assailed her, she never confided to Millie, but in her own room in Brunswick she looked them straight in the eye. "You are not beset like myself Millie, but the heart is prone to wander from God, even if there are no trying circumstances to tempt it. So let us each in our own sphere strive to renounce the devil and all his works."

Her optimistic view of the Christian life as a steady

SEA LAVENDER (Limonium nashii)
In late summer, the purple or lavender flowers in branching
sprays brighten Maine's shores and salt marshes.

progression gave her confidence, the sense that sustained struggle would bear blessed fruit, and "in the end one attain to a state of Godliness, from which stand point God will not permit us to fall...God will not allow us to be tempted beyond our strength. Happy thought! Comforting assurance!"

Although Kate's relationship with her Creator was a source of strength, her parents' health was a reminder that her earthly ties were loosening. "My Parents are both feeble. Father does not go out evenings now. How ought we to feel in view of losing our Parents, Millie? Ought we not bless God that we have had them in our tender and indiscreet days and also that they were spared till we were old enough to take care of them."

She felt no such consternation, however, about the loss of the sometime acquaintance with the "cunning little mouth." "Now — Millie: Do you remember that I told you that Mr. Wilson called on me when he first came here? He went away without coming to see me. There is no excuse for him; for he went to other places. I know one thing. Though he was quite pleasant, his company was not essential to my happiness."

Kate's brother John had married Maria Day, and another generation of Brunswick Furbishes had begun. The first was a new little Ben, his grandfather's counterpart with "large blue eyes."

The war was over and peace had come at last, making passage out of Brunswick simpler than ever. Then Kate began the habit of travel that was to characterize her life until the onset of old age. "I am

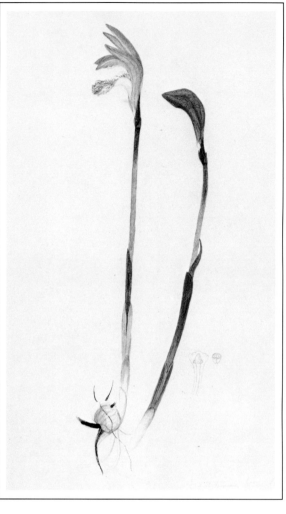

SWAMP PINK (Arethusa bulbosa)
Another name for this bog orchid, whose single leaf grows after it has flowered, is dragon's mouth.

sufficient. ... I am still in love with my relatives."

Kate was also full of serious plans, which she tempered with the qualifying remarks of a woman well aware of life's pitfalls. "If they are all well at home, and I am well here," she wrote, "I hope to be here a long time." Her own health, though, was uncertain. "I am suffering from Neuralgia at present, and feel almost impatient, though rather than be so, I strain every nerve to keep up good courage, and in spite of all keep about my work."

For despite the gay picture of life among the urban Furbishes that Kate presented to her cousin, she had gone to Boston for pursuits other than gossiping and visiting. "I am taking two lessons a week all the time," she wrote, "and practice the best part of every day." The struggle to paint had begun in earnest.

still in the City of 'nations'; still enjoying the busy whirl of city life," she wrote to Pamela from Hudson Street in Boston in January 1867. She reported that she was spending "a most delightful winter," gave some details of life among the Boston Furbishes, and tried to persuade Pamela to join her there. "Lizzie Day, who is here now, is perfectly carried away with you. Are you coming to Boston this winter? Wouldn't it be gay to be visiting with you 'round among our relatives? If two or three generations do intervene between each parent stalk and ourselves, as long as Furbish is the name 'tis

The habit of concentration emerged; the reality of pitting herself against society's odds became a pattern. Her opportunities in life would increase or decrease in direct ratio to her perception of them. "Lizzie Day says she never saw my equal. I do not know how that is, but I do not mean she shall see my superior in respect of determination to brave out pain."

Her determination, now focused on enriching the inner life of an unmarried woman still tied to her family, would surface later in the face of a broader challenge.

WHITE PINE (Pinus strobus)
This pencil drawing of Maine's "state flower" shows the clusters of
five long needles and the gently curving five-inch cones.

THREE

Toward a Maine Flora

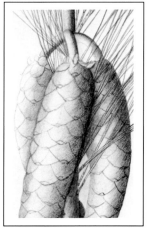

M aine, both as a district and as a state, was slow to yield an organized description of its flora. Ironically, the region had a head start on almost every other part of what is now the United States because it was visited in the mid-seventeenth century by a man who had an aptitude for observing nature and a flair for recording what he saw in words and pictures. He was an Englishman named John Josselyn.

Josselyn made two prolonged visits to the coast of Maine, the first in 1638 and 1639 and the second from 1663 to 1671. He was from Kent, and his father, Thomas, was an associate of Sir Ferdinando Gorges to whom Charles I granted the Province of Maine in 1639. One of Thomas's sons, Henry Josselyn, became an official under Gorges and lived for many years at Black Point in what is now the town of Scarborough. When John Josselyn sailed to North America, he apparently stayed with his brother Henry at Black Point. (There is now a bronze plaque dedicated to Henry Josselyn at the ninth tee on a Scarborough golf course.)

When John Josselyn returned to England after his second visit, he published two books, *New-England's Rarities Discovered in Birds, Beasts, Fishes, Serpents, and Plants of That Country* (in 1672) and *An Account*

of *Two Voyages to New-England* (in 1674). The first book is still of considerable interest to students of natural history. It is illustrated with woodcuts made from Josselyn's drawings of some of the "rarities," among them a sketch of a jewelweed plant, which he called the Humming Bird Tree. He drew a skunk cabbage, which he recognized as native to the new continent, and he seems to have been the first person to describe and sketch that plant. His description in *Rarities* is a model of botanical observation.

This Plant is one of the first that springs up after the White Hellibore, in the wet and black grounds, commonly by Hellibore, with a sheath or Hood like Dragons, but the pestle is of another shape, that is, having a round Purple Ball on top of it, beset (as it were) with Burs; the hood shoots forth immediately from the Root, before any Leaf appears, having a Green sprig growing fast by it, like the smaller Horse Tayl, about the latter end of April the Hood and Sprig wither away and there comes forth in the root a Bud, like the bud of the Walnut Tree, but bigger; the top of it is of a pale Green colour, covered with brown skins like an onion, white underneath the leaves, which spread in time out of the Bud, grow from the root with a stalk a Foot long, and are as big as the great Bur Dock Leaves, and

23

of the colour, the roots are many, and of the bigness of the steel of a Tobacco Pipe, and very white: the whole Plant scents as strong as a Fox; it continues to August.

Then, for almost two centuries there was silence. Maine attracted the attention of no skilled botanist. Indeed, the only plants native to the region that seemed to excite or interest anyone were the huge white pines cut from the forests and the stands of saltgrass harvested from the marshes as forage for the settlers' livestock. The early botanists in North America — men like Mark Catesby, John and William Bartram, André Michaux, and Peter Kalm — explored the Middle Atlantic states, the Southeast, and the wilds of Florida. Jane Colden, the daughter of gentleman naturalist Cadwallader Colden, botanized the countryside around the Coldens' home on the Hudson River and made something of an international stir with her plant drawings and collections. Their successors — Thomas Nuttall, David Douglas, and George Engelmann — crossed the Mississippi River and explored all parts of the American West, making known to the world the variety of plants. Meanwhile, botanically speaking, Maine remained terra incognita.

The first center of natural history study in this country was Philadelphia. Benjamin Franklin, of course, lived there, as did the Bartrams, and just about every important naturalist who lived in America or visited it during the first fifty years of the new nation's existence had close ties to that city. Charles Willson Peale's Museum in Philadelphia and the Philadelphia Academy of Natural Sciences became landmark institutions

WILD RED RASPBERRY (Rubus idaeus)
Aside from its color, this raspberry differs from its black relative in the young stems, which are densely covered with bristles.

in the history of American science. But as the nineteenth century progressed, the center of importance began to shift. Zoology and geology eventually found important sponsorship from the federal government in Washington. In botany the shift was to the north when John Torrey became the nation's outstanding botanist.

A New Yorker by birth, Torrey had earned his medical degree at the College of Physicians and Surgeons in New York City in 1818, and he later returned there to teach. From boyhood he had an intense interest in botany; while pursuing his medical studies he became a curator of the new Lyceum of Natural History in New York City. (Until recent times there was a close link between botany and medicine. Extracts of plants furnished physicians with the only cures, real or imagined, for most ailments.) Torrey collected plants indefatigably and compiled a catalog of plants in the vicinity. He was quick to grasp the outstanding ideas of the time. Although most American botanists still followed the plant classification system devised by the great eighteenth-century naturalist Carl Linnaeus, which was based on sexual characteristics such as pistilstamen counts, some advanced European botanists were beginning to find the system unwieldy. Torrey, absorbing the increasing fund of knowledge about plants, realized that the time had come for a change. He adopted the so-called natural system of classification based on broader principles of structure and function. He met with bitter opposition from American colleagues, but he won the day.

TWINFLOWER (Linnaea borealis)
A tiny fragrant plant related to the honeysuckle, it is named for the great botanist Linnaeus.

In his collecting and classifying, Torrey was joined by a young man who was first his protégé, then his partner, and ultimately the dominant figure in the history of American botany. Asa Gray was to pull together all the strands in a furious effort to describe the plant life of the United States in the middle of the nineteenth century and, in the process, shift the center of American botany to New England. Gray's family was originally from New England; his father was a farmer and tanner. Asa was born in 1810 in New York's Oneida County. Starting out on the road taken by so many American naturalists in the last century, he earned a medical degree, in his case at the Fairfield College of Physicians and Surgeons in Herkimer, New York.

While still a medical student, Gray read an article on botany in the *Edinburgh Encyclopedia* and responded almost as if it were a divine revelation. He bought a copy of the most popular botany manual of the day, written by Amos Eaton, and mastered its contents while impatiently awaiting the arrival of spring so that he could botanize in the nearby woods and fields. Medicine was forgotten; plants absorbed all his attention.

The young botanist was soon in touch with John Torrey. He went to New York City, moved in with the Torrey family, and set about learning nearly everything known at the time about his new subject. In 1836 the precocious Gray published the first of his popular textbooks, *Elements of Botany*. He made collections of

NEW ENGLAND ASTER (Aster novae-angliae)
When she found this plant at East Livermore and later at Poland Spring, Kate Furbish remarked, "I do not think it is common." Common in most of New England, it grows now in eleven Maine counties.

MOUNTAIN LAUREL (Kalmia latifolia)
This shrub, its clusters of white flowers vivid against the dark evergreen leaves,
reaches its northern limit in Maine.

plants in many parts of the country and familiarized himself with what other adventurous collectors of the day were doing. Meanwhile, he and Torrey began work on their ambitious *A Flora of North America,* the first part of which was published in 1842.

A trip to Europe, on which Gray met the celebrated botanists of Great Britain and the Continent, formed the basis of his international reputation. After returning to the United States, he wrote an article for the *American Journal of Science* that described important herbaria of Europe. In 1842 Harvard College appointed him Fisher Professor of Natural History,

and it was from Cambridge that he presided over American botany for the next four and a half decades.

The study of plants, though compulsory at the time for Harvard students, was in disarray at America's foremost academic institution. The botanical library and herbarium were insignificant. A small botanic garden in the care of a college gardener contained mainly a few local common plants. Gray changed all that. He gathered an extensive library and herbarium, which he later gave to Harvard on the condition that it erect a fireproof building to contain them. (The name of the herbarium — Harvard Herbarium — was later changed to Gray Herbarium.) He vastly improved the garden and adjacent greenhouses. Although he was not an eloquent teacher in the style of some of his Harvard colleagues, including the redoubtable Louis Agassiz, his well-organized and highly informative lectures won many converts to botany. For students who wanted to make botany a career he had some ready advice. "Study medicine, and if then you still want to be a botanist, go ahead. Your medicine will keep your botany from starving."

The papers written by Gray for scholarly journals — reviews, obituary notices, and the like — form a vivid history of botany during his lifetime. Collectors sent him their specimens from all over the country, leaving to

DWARF CRESS (Cardamine bellidifolia)
The unprepossessing alpine plant is currently found only on Mount Katahdin. This specimen was collected by Merritt Fernald.

and in my own fashion a Darwinian, philosophically, a convinced theist, and religiously, an accepter of the 'creed commonly called the Nicene,' as the exponent of the Christian faith." Certain developments of the time helped Asa Gray carry on his profound studies in the morphology, distribution, and classification of plants. Explorers were opening up the most remote areas of the globe; plant collectors were right behind them. Early in the century it had been rare for more than one plant in a hundred to survive a long journey. But now improved means of transportation and storage were ensuring the safe arrival of specimens at important herbaria, including Harvard's. In 1836 Nathaniel Bagshaw Ward

him the task of description and classification. As he compared North American plants with those collected in Europe and Asia, he became a pioneer in the study of the geographical distribution of plants. The work he did in this field proved to be of immense importance to Charles Darwin while writing *On the Origin of the Species by Means of Natural Selection.* Darwin corresponded with Gray and divulged to him the outlines of his momentous theory of evolution in advance of publication. In 1860 Gray wrote an influential thirty-two-page review of Darwin's book for the *American Journal of Science* and became Darwin's leading champion in the United States. He was, however, a theistic Darwinian. In his own book, *Darwiniana*, a collection of essays and reviews, Gray wrote, "I am scientifically

developed his Wardian Case, a small portable greenhouse built of wood and removable glass windows, which gave botanists a means of transporting and even cultivating plants in secure, closed shipping crates.

Another important step was the standardization of botanical nomenclature. In 1867 botanists from around the world gathered at the Paris International Congress and agreed on a code that would do away with the confusion in the scientific names of plants. The Paris Code stipulated that a plant could have only one technical name, that two different species or other groups could not bear the same name, and that a species was not validly named unless its specific name was assigned to a genus.

The general public will best remember Asa Gray for

PEARLY EVERLASTING (Anaphalis margaritacea)
Country people often gave plants far more vivid and appropriate names, such as pearly everlasting, than did learned scientists.

his important advances in satisfying the common craving to name things. In 1848 he published his *Manual of the Botany of the Northern United States.* In it, described in detail, were all of the region's plants known to science. The manual both responded to the growing popular interest in wild plants and contributed to the spreading of that interest, just as did the Peterson Field Guides for American birds almost a century later. From then on, men and women with a serious interest in plants could proceed into the field with the confidence that they could identify almost any specimen they found.

LOW SWEET BLUEBERRY (Vaccinium angustifolium)
This species is the one generally recognized as the edible fruit of Maine's barrens and the basis of its wild blueberry industry.

Nevertheless, while plant specimens flooded in to Asa Gray's herbarium from southern swamps and the deserts and mountains of the Far West, Maine's terrain was neglected by collectors. They may have reasoned that Maine was simply another northeastern state, where new varieties were unlikely to be found. In that supposition they would have been wrong, for Maine had a varied and attractive flora waiting to be tapped by adventuresome botanists.

There is a rule of thumb in biology that the diversity of species diminishes from the equator toward the poles. In other words, biologists tend to find more species of plants and animals in the tropics and subtropics than in temperate and subpolar regions. Though Maine may not have the density of species found in some southern parts of the United States, it is interesting botanically because it has a great variety of habitats in which plants grow. Few states display so many different kinds of terrain: offshore islands, a sinuous coastline ranging from beaches to salt marshes to rocky headlands, sandy plains, dense forests, river valleys, mountaintops, thousands of lakes and ponds, old fields, and cold sphagnum bogs.

Moreover, Maine lies in a transition zone. A most interesting botanical feature is that a portion of its flora is made up of southern plants that find their northernmost limits in the state. Conversely, many northern, Canadian plants find their southernmost limits in Maine. And, throughout the state, native plants mingle with such common European plants as dandelions, buttercups, and clovers inadvertently brought across the Atlantic Ocean in bags of grass and vegetable seeds by the early settlers. Additional plants, such as the black-eyed Susan, entered Maine with hayseed from the American West. This varied flora was present in the 1840s, waiting for botanists to describe it.

Maine's pioneering botanist was Aaron Young, Jr., a native of Wiscasset and a graduate of the Maine Medical School at Bowdoin. He tried his hand as a physician, a pharmacist, and a teacher while maintaining a lifelong interest in botany. At Bowdoin he was a friend of Franklin Pierce, and from 1863 to 1873 he served as United States consul in Brazil, where he collected plants.

Aaron Young conceived in 1840 the idea of preparing on a grand scale a work on the plants of Maine.

Through friends in the legislature he obtained $600 to make a botanical survey of the state. It was an ambitious project, in which Young planned to travel throughout Maine, collecting plants and selling the pressed specimens in sets of twenty volumes, each set priced at $100.

Young began his survey in 1847. He visited parts of the Maine coast and offshore islands, including Castine, Deer Isle, Isle Au Haut, Swans Island, and Kennebunk Beach, as well as forests in York County. He spent about two weeks with six companions in the Mount Katahdin area. At that time the ascent of Katahdin was a formidable challenge. Henry David Thoreau had climbed part of the mountain only the year before and remarked in his book, *The Maine Woods*, "Very few, even among backwoodsmen and hunters, have ever climbed it, and it will be a long time before the tide of fashionable travel sets that way." Thoreau, turned back by bad weather, had not made it to the top, but Aaron Young and his party did and brought back what a later botanist, Merritt Lyndon Fernald, called "the first representative collection of Katahdin plants."

But not much came of Young's ambitious proposal. The state legislature was not interested in funding any more surveys, and Young eventually gave up his plan. Only one volume of the proposed *Flora of Maine* was produced. This volume, bound in cloth with board covers, was 20 by 40 inches, with leaves measuring 19½ by 13½ inches. Young's statement on the first page stood as testimony to his hopes. "Flora of Maine, illustrated with specimens from nature, arranged according to the

SUNFLOWER (Helianthus sp.)
Its common name is a direct translation of its generic name. The original species is said to have come to North America from Peru.

natural system and containing descriptions of all the known indigenous plants growing in the State, giving their generic and specific characters, principal synonyms, places of growth, and time of flowering and occasional remarks, by Aaron Young, Jr., Bangor, Samuel S. Smith, Printers, 1848."

This was the year in which Asa Gray's *Manual of the Botany of the Northern United States* was published, but Young's volume did not receive the same wide distribution. In fact, it abruptly disappeared from history for more than a century, and no copy was known to exist until 1951, when a traveler found an excellent copy on sale in Antwerp, Belgium. This volume was purchased and given to Adelaide Pearson of Blue Hill, Maine, who realized its importance and presented it to the Gray Herbarium at Harvard University.

Ralph C. Bean, who was interested in Maine botany, described the volume in 1953 in *Rhodora*, the journal of the New England Botanical Club.

In the published volume sheets 13½ x 27 inches are folded and bound to make up the book. The first page contains the name of the plant, remarks as to the time of flowering, uses and often quotations from various authors such as Bigelow, Dewey, Torrey, and Emerson whose Trees and Shrubs of Massachusetts *had been published earlier. On the second page is pasted the actual specimen with its name. The volume is interleaved with thin paper…. there are thirty-nine species on thirty-three pages.*

During the next decade, collecting in Maine was

RED MAPLE (Acer rubrum)

This common tree, with its familiar reddish flowers, figures prominently in any survey of Maine's flora.

sporadic. The most notable event may have been another survey of Katahdin, this time in 1856 by Joseph Blake, a minister from Yarmouth, Maine. Blake's chief discovery was a tiny plant called the star saxifrage (*Saxifraga stellaris* var. *comosa*). Of this discovery Blake wrote:

I was glad to join my companions who were waiting for me at the top of the "Chimney." In making my way down this rugged precipitous descent while stopping a moment on a grassy ledge, I made a discovery of great interest to me: I found a little plant, not new indeed to science, but one that has a place in our [Maine's] flora only in consequence of my detecting it that day on the side of that towering mass of rocks. I brought away seven or eight specimens, all I found, indeed two of which I have; the others are in as many different herbariums. Botanists have visited the mountain since and sought for the plant, but unsuccessfully.

Susan C. Gawler, a Maine botanist of our own time, wrote: "Apparently Rev. Blake had no compunction either about collecting every plant he saw or about the fact that nobody had since seen the plant. Fortunately, his eyes weren't sharp enough to detect quite all of the individuals at this station." Kate Furbish never found a star saxifrage. Today, Mount Katahdin is the only place where it grows in the United States.

BLACK-EYED SUSAN (Rudbeckia serotina)
Kate Furbish found it "everywhere," though it is a western species brought to the East with clover seeds.

Finally, the state took an active part in the attempt to conduct a thorough botanical survey of its land. The Maine Board of Agriculture ordered a survey in 1861 and 1862 under the direction of George Lincoln Goodale. A native of Saco, Maine, Goodale was the son of Stephen L. Goodale, who served for many years as secretary of the Maine Board of Agriculture. George Goodale, like Asa Gray, later abandoned medicine for botany, which he taught at Bowdoin College and Harvard University. (On Gray's recommendation, Harvard appointed Goodale to be director of its botanic garden.)

At the outbreak of the Civil War, Goodale was still a medical student, and he accepted an offer to head the state's botanical survey. He collected plants in a number of areas, but his most important work was done in Aroostook County, in the far northeastern part of the state, which he revealed as being of exceptional botanical interest. Before setting out, Goodale noted that this northern tip of Maine, near the Saint John River, is nearly on the same parallel as part of Lake Superior. That prompted him to believe that he would find some western plants in the area, and he did. Later he wrote in his report to the Board of Agriculture:

One of the most attractive plants in this district is the Huronian tansy which I am able to add to the list

HURON TANSY (Tanacetum huronense)
*Growing in Maine only along the rivers of Aroostook County, this far northern plant
was found by the artist along a highway in Fort Kent, where it was abundant.*

of plants new to New England. It grows in patches of three or four feet square, and everywhere presents the same soft and finely dissected foliage. The odor is not so pungent as that of common garden tansy; it is rather like that of yarrow. A plant so characteristic of north-western vegetation, detected at a point so far East and in such plenty, suggests that a more careful survey of the section will develop many highly interesting facts.

As a result of this survey, Goodale compiled a check-list of all the known plants of Maine. It was published in two versions by the Portland Society of Natural History, which Goodale served as curator of botany while still attending medical school. The title of the first list published, in 1862, was *Catalogue of the Flowering Plants of Maine*. Six years later, that was combined with a list of nonflowering plants and appeared as *The Portland Catalogue of Maine Plants*.

Goodale deposited most of his plant specimens in the Portland Museum of Natural History, intending it to be a permanent record of his historic survey. Alas, in 1866 the museum burned and the herbarium was destroyed. George Goodale's collection no longer existed, and Aaron Young's *Flora* had disappeared. Aside from a few herbarium sheets scattered in certain collections, there was no tangible evidence in the scientific record of Maine's variety of flowering plants.

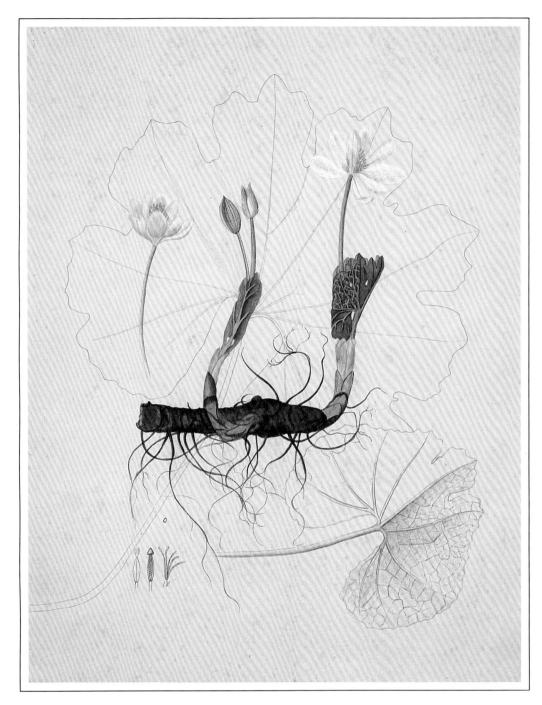

BLOODROOT (Sanguinaria canadensis)
Members of the poppy family produce an acrid liquid. The bloodroot's orange-red juice gives the plant its common name.

"Consider the Lilies of the Field"

*I*n early 1870 Kate Furbish, who was then thirty-six years old, was still living with her ailing parents in the family home on O'Brien Street. She was a diminutive woman, but by no means unprepossessing. Her square shoulders, penetrating gaze, and firm, distinct profile gave her a no-nonsense air.

Of her three brothers who had survived childhood, Frank (charming, already recognized as something of a ne'er-do-well) also was living at home; John and his wife, Maria, had established a home nearby with three children of their own; Edward had drowned in 1863 while swimming in the Androscoggin River, despite John's heroic efforts to rescue him. John had taken over the hardware business from his father, though prospects were no longer promising. The hopes for prosperity in Brunswick and the rest of Maine that had flourished in the early decades of statehood were not realized in the years following the Civil War. Between 1850 and 1870 Brunswick's population had decreased from 4,976 to 4,727.

Yet, as spring approached, John's spirits were by no means downcast. "It is doubtful whether so mild and open a winter was ever known," he wrote at the time. Then, on April 1, he exulted, "The month opens as

lovely as a May morning, and our streets are nearly free from snow." John's enthusiasm for the weather apparently kindled an affection for Brunswick's setting and history, for on March 30 he became cofounder and secretary of a local group, the History and Natural History Society.

That unusual Maine spring had a more profound effect on Kate, drawing her outdoors and into the woods and sandy meadows and along the riverbanks, which she ransacked for plants with the fervor of a pioneer botanist set loose in an unknown Eden. Nothing that had gone before suggested this feverish burst of collecting and painting. There had been a youthful interest in nature on long walks with family or friends, lessons and lectures in Boston, and scraps of paintings that were little more than earnest copies of popular illustrations of the day. But the record shows that in 1870 Kate produced an outpouring of scientific and artistic work unequaled at any other period of her life. As if by some miracle, the painter of Maine's flora suddenly appeared, at the height of her powers, fully equipped, fully matured.

During the spring and the months that followed, she wandered through the woods among the mayflowers, wood anemones, violets, bloodroot, and twinflowers; in fields among shepherd's purse, milkweed, hawkweed, blueberry, wild strawberry, thistle, and bluets; into the edges of swamps and ponds for skunk cabbage, marsh marigold, floating heart, bladderwort, and water arum; along the shore for seaside crowfoot and silverweed; and in small bogs for leatherleaf, Labrador tea, and pitcher plant. The countryside around Brunswick offered almost all the different habitats of the state. Having familiarized herself with the common species, she needed only to go farther afield to find the rarities.

It was no part of Kate Furbish's character to go into the woods simply as a Sunday stroller. She was bent on serious botanizing. She collected plants — some to dissect and analyze their flowering parts, others to press, catalog with detailed notations, and preserve on herbarium sheets. She made meticulous drawings of stems, leaves, roots, and blossoms, and even magnified seeds to portray them accurately on paper. At the moment of a plant's full bloom and purest color, she indicated its subtle tints and shadings by daubing touches of color within the penciled outlines in her sketches for the time when she would prepare a finished painting. Always, when she needed confirmation of a name or a technical detail, she turned to *Manual of the Botany of the Northern United States*, *How Plants Grow*, or other publications by the incomparable Asa Gray.

A clue to the preparation that brought Kate to this point of expertise appears in a letter written nearly a quarter century later to Mrs. Henry Johnson, the wife of a professor of modern languages at Bowdoin College, who had asked Kate to give her daughter lessons in botany. In her letter Kate declined to take on any teaching, but offered advice about the subject.

After an experience of 25 years in the botanical field without any teacher but Nature, save the privilege of listening to a few lectures delivered by Prof. Goodale to the teachers of Boston, I should give her the fields and juvenile books which treat the subject in a pleasing way. I am very fond of Gray's "How Plants Grow." I have never outgrown it, and I believe dear Mrs. Johnson that if you will interest yourself personally in the

SESSILE-LEAVED BELLWORT (Uvularia sessilifolia) and WOOD ANEMONE (Anemone quinquefolia)
Kate Furbish painted three separate plants here, each bearing a single flower. The bellwort here towers over the two anemones.

EARLY SAXIFRAGE (Saxifraga virginiensis)
*Though the leaves of the plant are basal, the flower-tipped stems branch when about
four inches high, then continue to grow and may reach a height of sixteen inches.*

matter, that you will be the best *teacher for your little
ones, you will surely be surprised as to how much you
will see, which probably has escaped your eyes.*

*I suggest that you commence with the A.B.C.'s of
the Science, viz by teaching the little ones the different
parts of the flower and their uses.... I do think that a
Herbarium adds to the interest, with the locality and
date attached.... The form and venation of leaves is
fully illustrated in "How Plants Grow." As time passes
the more difficult manuals will come to your aid naturally.... Gray's little volume can be bought anywhere.
This (and several other books for your readers) will be
sufficient for a long time. I love to study into the origin*

*of things, and you will find the kernel of the matter in
these interesting and inexpensive books.*

In *How Plants Grow* Asa Gray explained in clear,
concise prose the functions of every part of a plant. He
described stems and roots, leaves and flowers, and
these descriptions shaped Kate Furbish's approach to
the plants she found in the wild. That was especially
true of the blossom, whose sole purpose, as Gray
pointed out, is to produce a seed that will enable the
plant to reproduce itself.

"Flowers are most interesting to the botanist," Gray
wrote, "who not only admires them for their beauty,
the exquisite arrangement and forms of their parts, and

TRAILING ARBUTUS (Epigaea repens)
*Last year's leaves cling to this plant, whose fragrant flowers often
appear before the last of New England's snows are gone.*

PIPSISSEWA (Chimaphila umbellata)
The flowers are among the latest of the spring woodland plants to open,
while the leaves are evergreen.

the wonderful variety they exhibit, but also sees in the blossoms much of the nature or character of each plant, and finds in them the best marks for distinguishing the sorts of plants and the family they belong to."

Kate Furbish's achievement in painting plants was to show how the parts of their flowers in an astonishing diversity of shapes — the three symmetrical petals of the trillium, for instance, or the five asymmetrical petals (forming a kind of winged pouch) of the pea — are related in their function. The beauty of flowers, as Gray had demonstrated and Kate accepted, was utilitarian.

Utilitarian, in their message as well as in their function. At the beginning of *How Plants Grow*, Asa Gray had set a Biblical text for his young readers.

Consider the lilies of the field, how they grow; they toil not, neither do they spin: And yet I say unto you, That even Solomon in all his glory was not arrayed like one of these.

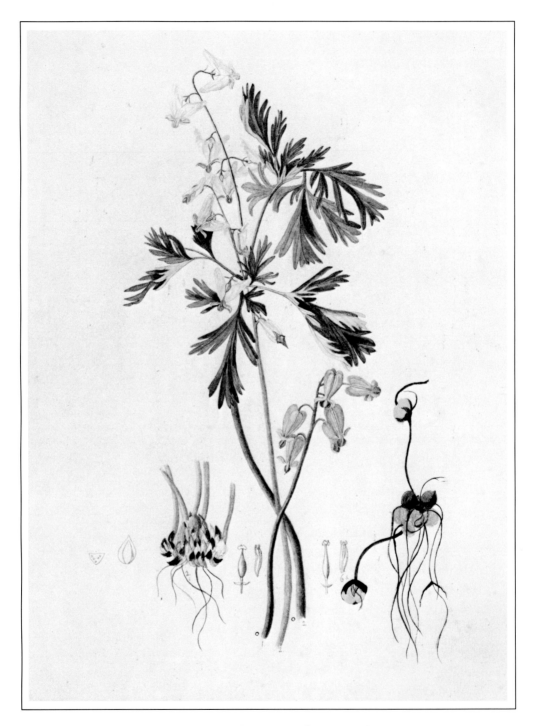

SQUIRREL CORN (Dicentra canadensis), No. 1,
and DUTCHMAN'S BREECHES (Dicentra cucullaria), No. 2.
The two plants, each with a name that describes one of its parts, have similar leaves.
The roots of the first are thought to resemble corn; the flowers' shape provides a name for the second.

Gray went on to make the message plain, a message that not only young readers but most of their elders of the time, Kate Furbish included, were inclined to accept.

Our Lord's direct object in this lesson of the lilies was to convince the people of God's care for them. Now, this clothing of the earth with plants and flowers — at once so beautiful and so useful, so essential to all animal life — is one of the very ways in which He takes care of his creatures. And when Christ himself directs us to consider with attention, the plants around us — to notice how they grow, — how varied, how numerous, and how elegant they are fashioned and adorned — we shall surely find it profitable and pleasant to learn the lessons which they teach.

When Kate set off for the nearby woods in April 1870, to search out the first blooms of spring, she was well prepared for whatever plants she encountered. As he was for thousands of other New Englanders, Asa Gray became in a sense her companion in discovery. The authority of his word was the foundation on which she would build her collection.

Kate was part of an old tradition. Almost from the beginning of European settlement in New England, men and women had gone to the woods to collect the earliest spring plants. Her father had known the wild flowers, and doubtless his knowledge had been passed down to him from older generations. Much of the traditional plant collecting was extremely practical, for plants were used in cooking and for medicinal purposes. The list of plants believed to cure one ailment or another seems endless. Wild ginger was collected for its

WILD GINGER (Asarum canadense)
The artist collected this species in Caribou on her trip to Aroostook County.

root, from which an infusion was made to treat flatulence, dropsy, and various ills of the chest. Fresh leaves of the trout lily, when applied as a poultice, worked their wonders on tumors and swellings but when ingested were supposed to cure hiccups.

The all-purpose plant may have been bloodroot. The benefits of its root were described recently by Judith B. Johnson in her book, *The Heritage of Our Maine Wildflowers:*

"*Medicinal properties:* Cathartic, diuretic, emetic, enemenagogue, expectorant, febrifuge, rubefacient, sedative, tonic. Small dose is stimulating to the digestive organs and is tonic and expectorant. Large dose is sedative, emetic, narcotic. Overdose can be very harmful.

"*Useful in treating:* Colds, coughs, croup, laryngitis, pneumonia, bronchitis, asthma, indigestion; heart, liver, lung, and kidney problems, nervous irritation, ringworm, skin diseases, syphilitic problems, and catarrh."

Ultimately, the spring flowers provided a tonic not so much for the body as for the spirit. There was a genuine craving after the long New England winter for the sight of new life pushing up through the forest litter as the last snows melted away. Nineteenth-century American poets sang of the woodland flowers with an intensity that reflected their own hunger for the first fugitive glints of color in the dappled light of the woods.

These woodland plants needed to seize their moment. Responding to increasing warmth and light, they made haste to spring up and blossom before the trees put forth their leaves and shut out light for the rest of the summer. Their fragility, their fleeting blossoms, their

NORTHERN DOWNY VIOLET (Viola fimbriatula)
*Kate Furbish painted ten different species of violets — blue, white, and yellow — finding them throughout
the state and on islands offshore, in sandy fields, sphagnum bogs, steep rocky hillsides, and damp woods.*

TROUT LILY (Erythronium americanum)
The leaves, mottled with brown, give the plant its name.

seeming spunk as they confronted the harsh weather of early spring made them especially precious to all who tramped the woods. They were everyone's favorites, as expressed by Charlotte Coues, the mother of the ornithologist Elliott Coues, writing in the *New Hampshire Gazette* in 1853: "We love flowers — some of them. Not the stiff, high-colored flaunting things which autumn gives us, but, more than all others, the gentle, fragrant modest blossoms of spring, with their delicate tints, their graceful tender forms, their refreshing perfumes."

The spring flowers — often tiny, sometimes barely visible above the forest litter or a scrap of melting snow — obviously charmed Kate Furbish, too. Her paintings reflect a sympathetic eye. There was wonder in her encounters with flowers in the forest in places where traces of winter clung. Yet there was something more. She had learned to look at the parts of flowers with the eye of a practiced botanist. She approached the woods purposefully, willing to accept the unusual, but determined to locate what she knew was there. Furthermore, she was never content to sketch a species only once, consider it "finished," and move on to another species. She captured plants in their diversity.

Part of the botanical education of Kate Furbish, like

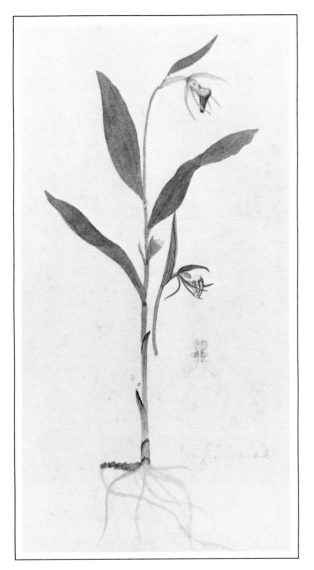

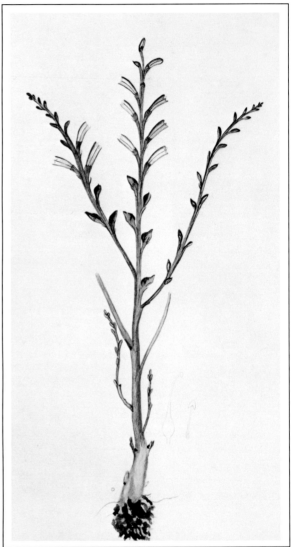

RAM'S-HEAD LADY'S SLIPPER
(Cypripedium arietinum)
The artist found the short-lived bloom of this plant fully open.

BEECHDROPS (Epifagus virginiana)
A parasite that feeds on the roots of beech trees, it is found by the collector among its more spectacular neighbors on the forest floor.

that of any other serious naturalist, lay in discovering how plants are linked to place and time. To most people, woods are simply a place where there are trees. The careful observer, however, knows that woods are composed of a variety of natural settings, dependent first on the underlying strata of rock, elevation, and soils. A well-drained rocky slope obviously produces vegetation quite different from the moisture-laden soil of a stream's bank. As we have seen, Kate Furbish found in the vicinity of Brunswick a natural microcosm of the rest of Maine. So, too, in the woods she found a surprising variety of habitats.

WHITE BANEBERRY (Actaea pachypoda)
"Bane" refers to the poisonous white berries of this woodland plant.

naturalist, no spring is complete without a sighting of the most spectacular of the northern orchids, the lady's slipper.

Kate Furbish obviously delighted in the fragile beauty of hepaticas and anemones, but she was just as fascinated by more unorthodox blossoms. About such plants Mrs. William Starr Dana, in her nineteenth-century field guide *How to Know the Wild Flowers*, commented: "Certain flowers might be grouped under the head of 'vegetable cranks.' Here would be classed the evening primrose, which only opens at night, the closed gentian, which never opens at all, and the wild ginger, whose odd unlovely flower seeks protec-

Rich woodland soils, dry rocky places, well-drained and sandy open areas, the muck of low, wet spots, the banks of rushing streams, stands of hardwood trees where the sun poured through before the trees were fully leaved, and dim coniferous groves where light seldom penetrated the evergreen foliage — all yielded their own types of plants to her inquiring eye. She even found a large number of the family of plants associated by most people with the tropics — the orchids. For a

tion and hides its head upon the ground as if unwilling to challenge comparison with its more brilliant brethren." Each of these curiosities in the May woods required close observation for their various structures to be understood.

In her attempt to reproduce on paper the plants that she found in the landscape, Kate Furbish clearly agreed with an earlier authority: "Even Solomon in all his glory was not arrayed like one of these."

VIRGINIA CREEPER (Parthenocissus quinquefolia)
This climber bears tendrils ending in disks that adhere to surfaces that will support it.
It would have been seen by Kate Furbish on her travels to the Mid-Atlantic states.

Transition

Kate Furbish's mother and father died within a month of each other in early 1873, and on May 19 she wrote in her journal, "At 7:30 A.M. I left the home of my life."

It was a wrenching departure. Thirty-eight years old and suddenly orphaned, she left the family home on O'Brien Street, which had always been her haven, and found herself adrift and moving into an uncertain future. She had grown up in a houseful of brothers for whom there were all sorts of possible careers in commerce, agriculture, crafts, and the military. For a woman of Kate's time and class, however, there were few practical openings aside from teaching and nursing. Nor were there the opportunities for marriage that had existed in New England before the Civil War, which had killed many of the young men and whose aftermath had sent others west to find new challenges.

"This decimation of the male population left a large surplus of women in the East," Jean Strouse wrote in her book, *Alice James: A Biography*. Strouse went on to show how the number of surplus women rose in Massachusetts in the Civil War era and how the number of marriages declined, though there was a surplus of men in the West. And she added, "Throughout the

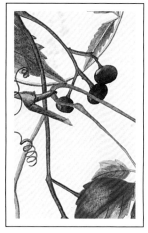

East the surplus of women created considerable anxiety about spinsters and amused celebration of what Theodore Parker, a noted Unitarian minister, called 'the glorious phalanx of old maids.'"

At this time Kate Furbish's faith in her beloved Furbish clan justified itself, giving her time to rearrange her life and mark out a rewarding future. Her mother's youngest brother had married a southern woman and in 1843 moved to New Castle, Delaware. In Kate's bereavement she was invited to visit the Delaware branch of the Lane family. A conservative person in the most profound sense of the phrase and imbued with a religious nature and a reverence for ancestors and tradition, she found the invitation a welcome solution to her troubles.

When she set out for New Castle, she began a journal that gives nearly a day-by-day account of her life during the transition year, 1873. Almost no detail of the new life escaped her attention or failed to elicit an opinion. Banks and churches, the building of ships and the manufacture of mustard, the methods of sewage disposal and the use of whipping posts, the rudeness of statesmen and the excitement of seaside resorts — all came under her notice and were occasions for comment. From the travels of that year emerged a woman with a sense of direction.

SWAMP BUTTERCUP (Ranunculus septentrionalis)
The genus name, meaning "little frog," is apt because many members of this large family live in wet places. There are more than thirty species in the northeastern corner of the United States.

Kate's descriptions of the places she visited show little literary skill, but display instead a mind whose interests and curiosity were especially broad for a woman at that time. The descriptions suggest her father's influence and a family environment in which she had been exposed since girlhood to a great variety of political, commercial, and technological topics. She found New Castle smaller than Brunswick "but built like a city of brick," in contrast to the frame construction of northern New England, and she acquired an extraordinary amount of information about the town during her first forty-eight hours. She informed herself about the local schools' sources of income, the plight of the blacks ("the *Colored* children have *nothing* provided for their education"), and the names and functions of the six courts held in town.

Her comments on the customs of New Castle residents indicate that she was flexible in the face of ways that were strange to a New Englander. "The ladies run about the streets bare-headed, and bare-handed, and sit on the steps and side-walks in summer," she wrote, "Which seems odd to us, but a custom which I shall undoubtedly enjoy." On an excursion during which she was the only woman interested in visiting a spice mill, she learned that the best-selling item was a yellow mustard, made without any mustard seed at all but popular among "fastidious ladies who will not try *brown* mustard for their tables, because it does not look nice." Even more fascinating to her was the existence of a public whipping post in the local jail yard, one of only two left in the nation and, she noted, a "relic of barbarism" — but one she determined to see for herself.

Indeed, Kate Furbish sought out relics of all kinds, particularly old churches. She made a sketch in her journal of New Castle's Immanuel Church, built in 1689, whose stout stone walls and tall spire had been maintained with a proper regard for their antiquity. "I feel that it will be a great comfort to me to worship in this church, made sacred by age," she wrote. "How much more so to those whose ancestors for generations have knelt at the same chancel-rail to partake of the Holy Eucharist!"

In midsummer she and her Aunt Mollie fled New Castle's heat to spend a week at Cape May, New Jersey, then one of the country's most fashionable resorts. The voyage was by sea, which disappointed her by its monotonous calm, and at first she was put off by the ten thousand visitors who uncomfortably crowded Cape May's beaches and hotels. Nor, in the evening, did she think that the belles from Baltimore lived up to their reputation for beauty.

Yet Kate was soon swept up in the excitement of the resort. There was a stabbing and a near-drowning at the beach. She was enchanted by the band concerts; every large hotel presented two of them a day. Some of her new acquaintances felt sorry for her because she did not swim, but she remarked in her journal that the drowning of her brother Edward had robbed her of any desire for "sea bathing."

Kate wandered the beach alone, gathering pebbles and wild peas, and watching the passing parade. "I envied the comical looking beings as they emerged from the various bathing-houses. Almost all looked

WILD PLUM (Prunus nigra)
Either in Maine or Delaware, Kate waited for spring to bring these trees into spectacular bloom.

VIRGIN'S BOWER (Clematis virginiana)
This graceful climbing plant works its way upward by wrapping its leaf stalks around the supporting vegetation.
It is named for a state far south of Maine, yet was familiar to Kate Furbish on her northern surveys.

ugly, but the gentleman and lady are still distinguishable, from the coarse and vulgar who were well represented there. I do not expect to see such a body of fantastics together again, 'till I meet with them here. It is fun to see a thousand people playing in the water together: old men and women, young men and maidens, children, babes of six months (Negroes not excluded) — all taking their baths. It is a Panorama which will never pass from my mind."

Although she hoped to visit Cape May again, on the last day she seemed to feel that her departure was a permanent farewell. "I think it has been the most entertaining week of my life," she wrote. "So new; so varied. All nations represented — The wealth of the Southern and Middle States. Fine equipages, elegant attire, beauty and deformity: good breeding and vulgarity; silk and muslin; Jew, Gentile; saint and sinner; (*More* sinners than saints, I thought.) I am lost in wonder as I think of all the ins and outs of this rendezvous of the Nations."

The other trips from New Castle that summer were mainly short excursions to the countryside for botanizing. Apparently her journal was not for the eyes of fellow botanists because, though she mentions discovering several wild flowers that were new to her, she fails to name them. The osage orange and the hawthorne hedges, though, delighted her.

"As I wander after flowers," Kate wrote, "I feel that I would persuade all when looking abroad on the bursting buds, the unfolding leaves, the embryo-fruits of early summer, to read on every petal, every pod, the soul cheering invitation — 'Lift up your eyes on high and behold, *who* hath created these things that bringeth out their hosts by number? He calleth them all by names by the greatness of His might.'"

During the fall there were trips to New York and Philadelphia, and then a return to New Castle for the holidays. As 1873 ended — "a year which has brought more change and sorrow to my heart, than any other ever did" — Kate's thoughts were necessarily turned briefly toward home. She recorded memories of her

GREEN ASH (Fraxinus pennsylvanica)
Kate Furbish's interest in trees intensified during her travels, and she asked that specimens of their pistillate and staminate flowers be sent to her in Delaware.

53

early life with her parents in Brunswick, but a sudden snowfall at New Castle prompted cheerier thoughts of New England. As she helped to prepare the Christmas decorations, she noted, "The wreathing of the 'Holly' does not inspire me as the Fir does at home, for it is scentless, and so destitute of Christmas associations in my mind."

The most memorable days of that transitional time probably were the ones she spent in the nation's capital. The New York express train that Kate Furbish and her Aunt Mollie boarded in Baltimore arrived in Washington on the evening of January 23, 1874, for what she described in her journal as "my first visit to W." They were met at the station by Benjamin Janvier, one of Aunt Mollie's Washington relatives. He was attentive and thoughtful as he guided them through official Washington on their way to the Janvier home. The first building he pointed out, the Capitol, was accepted by Kate as the focus of her trip. "The pictures I have seen of the Public-buildings have made all things familiar." she wrote.

Kate and her aunt were made comfortable in the stylish Janvier household, where she learned, "They have four meals regularly besides a night lunch for all who wish it." She found out that Harriet, a black house-servant "who attends to my wants here," had been Mrs. Robert E. Lee's dressing maid for nine years. "She shows her training," commented the abolitionist but not egalitarian Kate Furbish.

After an eight o'clock breakfast the following morning, "We visited the President's house, with which I was fully satisfied," even to approving the new decorating scheme for the East Room. "The East-room in its new dress of crimson and mouse color seems perfect in its appointments — while the Blue-room is furnished in most exquisite taste." Her approving eye was not that of a mere tourist, for later that month she would be a guest in the East Room at a reception given by President Ulysses S. Grant. She added her two cents' worth to the current controversy about whether to replace the President's house, which was not yet officially called the White House. "If I was a man I should

HEDGE BINDWEED (Convolvulus sepium)
*A member of the morning glory family. It was collected by
Kate Furbish in Maine, and she saw it just as often
on her trip to the Mid-Atlantic states.*

vote against erecting a new one; for what *anyone* can want more elegant apartments to live in I do not see; if *it is* called 'a National Disgrace,' my view is the exception." With that issue behind her, she pushed on to other sights.

"From there, we went to Corcoran's Gallery, a collection of paintings and statuary thrown open to the public by a rich gentleman of the city. I saw but few remarkable paintings. The protrait of Wm. W. Corcoran, the donor, by C. L. Elliott is life size and very fine. One by Paul Weber — a scene in the Catskills, and one by O. Von Thoren — The Last Days, were the only pictures which I particularly admired." In her discussion of a collection of flower paintings at the Corcoran, her opinions were based on something more than caprice. "Flower pieces by E. Gustave Couder were admirable as works of Art, but the backgrounds were too elaborate, making the subjects of the pictures subordinate to [them] which is poor composition." Here she was applying the criteria that she had no doubt found prevalent in classes and discussions. She reserved her one aesthetic outburst for an enormously popular sculptor of the day, Hiram Powers. "My greatest pleasure was found in the statuary. Powers' Greek Slave (The original) I saw for the first time. Proud am I, for that we can claim the author of that chaste work of art for a countryman. Faultless! To some a woman profaned. To me, a woman glorified."

That afternoon, "on a decision of the moment," Kate and her aunt attended Ford's Theater for a performance of *The American Cousin* with "Southern, the great comedian." She admitted to "having no fancy for comedy," though she added a historical note: "Lincoln was witnessing this play when he was assassinated."

There were callers that evening at the Janvier home, as there were every evening. It was a good chance for Kate to voice tentative opinions and test them in the social sphere before entrusting them to her journal. And so she wrote from day to day:

Jan. 26: The Capitol interior exceeded my expectations.... The Senate in session was dignified and very attentively listening to the Senator from Kentucky, who

WILD MINT (Mentha arvensis)
Wherever she traveled, Kate Furbish would have found members of this common family of plants.

is called a very smart man.... *When we entered the House [of Representatives] I noticed the confusion of the "Reps" moving about and talking. Counted five negroes occupying seats.... Jas. G. Blaine occupied the Speaker's seat. Also saw Alex Stephens of Georgia, a dilapidated looking old gentleman, but looking the aristocrat, all over; he was wrapped in a cloak and covered as to his head with a close silk cap, he looked too tired to be there. In passing let me say that the sheep are separated from the goats by a broad aisle, the two political parties occupying different sides of the room. Let their ranks designate them....*

Jan. 28: Morn. dull. Started out alone to shop a little, and go to the Capitol. The sun broke out in a short time and my walk down Penn. Av. was delightful. I reached the Capitol. I spent more than an hour looking over views.

Afterwards, I went to the Senate for a short time, and had the good fortune to hear [Charles] Sumner's and [Frederick T.] Frelinghuysen's voices for a moment. There is so much moving and whispering that unless one has a full clear voice it is impossible to hear. The last but by no means the easiest task of the day, was the climb to the Dome of the Capitol. I feared it would not pay — but I knew it must be done, in order to do W. So with but little courage I began my ascent on foot and alone. But I gained courage as I ascended, for it is not difficult, so fine is the long flight of steps and the machinery of the structure, so attractive, being mostly of iron, well painted, and so massive, it says to the beholder, I was built to last forever. Well, 325 steps brought me to the 3rd Balustrade, where I joined those who were admiring the frescoes. I desired to see them near, and expected they would suffer, but they do not, gigantic tho' the figures are. By the nearest approach, they are distant still and I felt paid. I spent an hour there and in enjoying the birds-eye view which the elevation gave me of the city — I feel glad that I went, and went alone. There are some things and places which I can enjoy better alone.

Kate Furbish had commemorated the first anniversary of her mother's death on January 27 by spending an hour alone. A few days later she put formal mourning behind her.

Jan. 31: This aft. went out on Penn. Av. to adorn myself for the Literary Reception given by Hon. Horatio King — an assistant P.M. General under Buchanan and Pierce, but now a private gentleman. When I was introduced as from Maine, he gave me a warm pressure of the hand, saying "Though I have lived here since 1818, I am always glad to welcome people from my native state." I asked "Where?" He replied yankee-like, "Where?" I replied, "Brunswick," He said, "Paris." He is said to be a man of rare culture.... Hon. J. G. Blaine of Maine was present, but I had no disposition to be introduced. I remember too well, the ungentlemanly manner in which he attacked a member of our State Legislature (Mr. Gould of Thomaston) to admire him. We bade our host good evening at 10:30. This is the first company which I have appeared in since my dear Parents passed away — and though I went against my heart's inclinations I came to see W. It seems necessary to see its social as its political life. It realizes, thus far, my fondest anticipations. I am favorably situated to see W., visiting thro' Aunty's family in the first circles here, and I try to see all I can and improve by what I see and hear....

Feb. 2: Mr. J. took me to the President's Levee [a formal] reception — a jam, and a rush. I saw many of the Foreign Legation — and the elite generally. The Marine Band afforded me more pleasure than the people. The East-room looks magnificently lighted. However, I was not particularly fascinated with the affair, tho' I was introduced to some agreeable people.

Two days later Kate Furbish paid a visit to one of the most talked-about figures of the day in Washington, the sculptor Vinnie Ream. When a girl of only eighteen, she had received a highly prized commission from Congress to create the statue of the recently martyred President Lincoln that still stands in the Capitol rotunda. The commission, the first ever granted by the federal government to a woman artist, aroused a great deal of jealousy and tongue wagging over the achievement of the vivacious, confident young

COW PARSNIP (Heracleum maximum)
The flower clusters, or umbels, of this big, wooly species are eight inches across and the leaves often a foot wide, giving the plant prominence in the landscape.

57

woman, and Kate looked forward to a tour of her studio with understandable curiosity.

Feb. 4: I enjoyed my visit to Miss Ream's very much. I am not pleased with her statue of Lincoln at the Capitol and had a desire to see her other works of art, and was pleased with several. On entering the room I at once noticed a bas-relief of a Maine man, a Mr. Rice, which pleased her very much. Her statue representing the "West" is pleasing, also a Cherub and two hands in marble. She told me Jessie Frémont [wife of explorer John Charles Frémont] sat for one of them. We visited all stages of her work, from her finished marble and plastercasts, to the head of Chief Justice Chase which is still in the clay. I had never seen this branch of art before in this incipient state, and was much interested.

The range of Kate Furbish's interests is demonstrated by subsequent entries in her journal while in Washington.

Feb. 9: Mr. Henry Nicholson came and took me to the Marine-Barracks and Navy Yard.... The visit to the various machine shops was a matter of great interest to me. The copper mill in particular where I saw copper rolled into large sheets, and following the process thro' saw some of these sheets turned into solid nails of different sizes with U.S. stamped on the head of each (and all done at one stroke, 60 in a minute by hand, and 250 in a min. by steam.) I saw a "Trip-hammer" in one of the shops which weighs more than 16,000 lbs. and Mr. N. told me that it made the whole yard tremble, when it dropped with its full force on. I think he told me there are 40 acres enclosed. Perfect neatness prevails everywhere. Everything used in War at Sea is manufactured there....

Feb. 10: Mrs. Janvier went with me to the Medical Museum and left me there to enjoy the "horrors," as she expressed it. I spent an hour and a half there and was very much interested.... The effect of disease in almost every conceivable form is represented there, preserved in Alcohol. Legs, arms, hands, feet mangled by shot and shell. Diseased livers, hearts, lungs, kidneys, bladders. Hands with one finger gone, others with all gone, the same with feet, but they were bloodless, and presented so different an appearance from what they would be on the bodies of the living, that they did not affect me in their painless condition. The cancers and tumors which I saw — the condition of the kidneys with Bright's disease consuming them, and the enlarged condition of the heart from various causes seemed more a source of wonder to me than the skulls and other bones of the body shattered by shell and shot — for it proved to me

SWEETBRIER (Rosa eglanteria)
The blossoms of this species, growing on long, arching stems, are smaller than those of most other roses. It was one of the "old friends" from Maine that Kate Furbish would have found in Delaware.

that we must die, and that death on the battlefield is not the only kind of death to be dreaded....

Feb. 11: Mrs. Dr. Beale [wife of the surgeon general of the Navy and cousin to Aunt Mollie] and I went to the Convent of the Visitation in Georgetown. We presented ourselves at the door of the cloistered convent, rang the bell, and a little window in the main door flew open, and at the grate appeared one of the most interesting faces which I ever saw, not young, but extremely lovely, and on the casement lay a perfect hand, small, white, ringless, perfect. She wore the black veil indicating that she had taken the vow of seclusion for life. She kindly and pleasantly directed us to the public entrance ...into an inner hall where we were met by another black [garbed] nun, sweet-faced like the other. (And I thought to myself, can we make our faces what we choose?) To her Mrs. Beale made known her errand and asked for several "sisters." Two of the same were living who taught Mrs. B. 30 years ago ...I have no desire to be a nun. Out in the world I will try to do my work well, and they must do theirs in their way, and God grant that we may reach the same goal and hear the same welcome home from the Savior of all who call upon him in sincerity.

Kate Furbish's relentless probe of Washington life continued. The hothouses connected to the Capitol delighted her, for many tropical plants were in flower, especially the gum arabic tree. "It is flaming scarlet and looks like a delicate miniature bush." She made a visit to the offices of Ferdinand V. Hayden, famous for his surveys of the Yellowstone and other regions of the West. There she indulged her passion for stereopticons and bought a dozen views of the Colorado River. She spent a morning at the Smithsonian Institution, comparing the bird collection there unfavorably with the Agassiz collection in Cambridge, although "there were many more stuffed animals.... I am so fond of Natural History in all its forms." She closed her day at the hothouses of the nearby Agriculture Department, where she "filched Ferns from Uncle Sam, only as mementos."

Sundays, considered by some a day for a more retiring mood, Kate gave over to exhaustive tours of Washington's churches, attending no fewer than four services on a single day. Four meals a day continued to be served at the Janviers' busy table, and callers continued to arrive each evening, but Kate's correspondence did not suffer from her Washington schedule. She kept her various friends informed, and received five letters in reply on a single day.

On February 12, several weeks after her Aunt Mollie had returned to New Castle, Kate wrote in her journal: "I have been here three weeks, and tomorrow if it is pleasant must return the calls which I've rec'd (22), and pack my trunk for New Castle after a most delightful visit among strangers. I have been highly favored thro' Aunty's relatives since I came to W. and should have attended more of the receptions had I not been in black — and glad to make it an excuse for declining. I have found it a protection many times."

Clearly, Kate knew how to make the best use of protective coloration in maintaining her privacy. She would need other, more aggressive, qualities to find a rewarding role for herself in the years ahead.

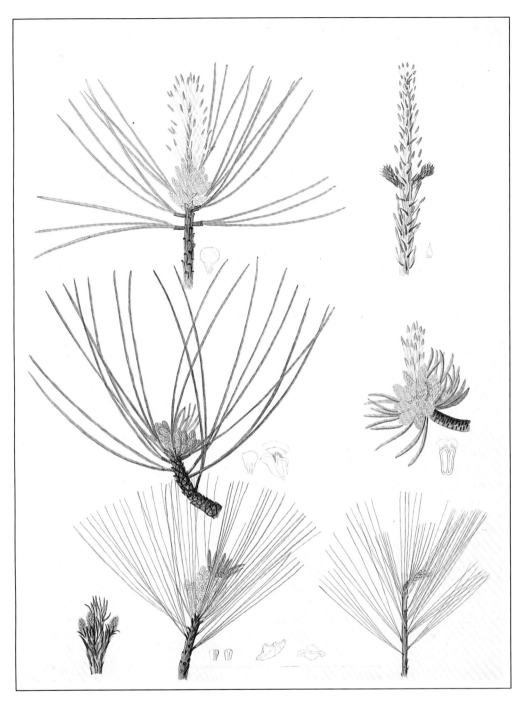

PITCH PINE (Pinus rigida), RED OR NORWAY PINE (Pinus resinosa), WHITE PINE (Pinus strobus)
from top to bottom
Kate Furbish depicted the male and female flowers of three of Maine's pine trees.
Like many of her other tree portraits, this one was executed solely in colored pencil.

"Your Botanical Friend"

Early in 1875 Kate Furbish found a new home. Almost predictably in her close-knit clan, it came to her from her brother John. She paid him $2,800 for a house and lot on the south side of Brunswick's Lincoln Street, property that he had picked up about a dozen years earlier and which nearly abutted from behind the old family house on O'Brien Street.

There was something straightforward about her new home. It was a modest white frame building in a row of more elaborate houses, with a back porch and a second story composed mainly of a sunny chamber, where Kate kept both her bed and her easel. She would never think of it as a home in the same sense as the family house on O'Brien Street. It was to be a place of work, a repository for the collection of thousands of pressed plants she obtained throughout the state, and a temporary storage place for her already considerable body of botanical watercolors. The house was also to be a haven for her in the intervals of almost incessant travels during the coming years. She sought "home" in the warmth of the friends' and relatives' families with whom she stayed when she traveled outside Brunswick.

The little house held symbolic importance, though. Until then, Kate had been seen in Victorian terms chiefly as the unmarried daughter of Benjamin and Mary Lane Furbish. Even after their death she had extended the identification, remaining the daughter in mourning, putting off the step of becoming a single, independent woman until she had time to prepare her new stance in society. Now she took on a clearly defined identity: she became a mature woman who owned a house in the center of town and pursued an active interest in art and science. Furthermore, at some unknown time she resolved to collect and paint all the flowering plants of Maine.

Before the deed for the new property was in her hands, Kate left Brunswick to spend the winter in Boston, where she boarded first on Fremont Street and later on Shawmut Avenue. In fact, she seems never to have stayed in any one place for long. That winter she spent three weeks in Boston with Mrs. W. C. Currier and a week each with Mrs. J. F. Frisbie, Mr. A. S. Flint, and Mrs. E. E. Fitch. And she made trips outside the city to visit her cousin Meda, and call on friends in Newton Center.

"I am heartily glad to have a home once more," she wrote to a friend at about this time, "but if I was rich enough should prefer to make it in Boston where I could have access to the Libraries and other advantages

VIPER'S BUGLOSS (Echium vulgare)
*Furbish decided to represent this large plant, taken in Farmington,
in two separate paintings. The top half appears here, showing
the blue flowers (with long red stamens prominent)
that blossom one at a time on the branches.*

which even a college town so far away from a larger city does not afford."

There was the usual round of social calls, but the chief attraction of Boston was those advantages, which she was eager to use. She attended the studio of a Mr. Filembe and sketched various objects in an attempt to increase her skill at painting from the living plant. In the colder months she visited horticultural exhibits to study flowers and haunted Boston's picture stores and galleries. "Boston is *richer* today in Art (as far as I am a judge) than either of the large cities [New York and Philadelphia] which I visited."

A woman she often called on was Anne Jackson, like herself a winter refugee from Brunswick and a collector of wild plants. Over the years Anne Jackson was of service to Kate in a number of ways, helping her to add plants to her collection and conferring with her on problems of identification. The greatest service of all was to introduce Kate to a man with whom she was to form one of the two most important professional friendships of her life. That man was George Edward Davenport.

Davenport had been born into an old Boston family in 1833, so he was only a year older than Kate Furbish. He was a successful businessman in Boston, a manufacturer of picture frames. Yet he had many other interests. Before the Civil War he had been active in the antislavery movement; later he was involved in labor reform. His deepest interest lay in natural history, especially in studying ferns, about which he wrote many scientific papers and acquired a considerable reputation as an authority. He was a founding member of the New England Botanical Club, a life member of the Massachusetts Horticultural Society, and (later) a fellow of the American Academy of Arts and Sciences. When Kate Furbish met him, he had just moved with his wife and eight children from South Boston to Medford, where he served on the school board and did pioneer conservation work on the Middlesex Fells.

Davenport's life was proof that during the nineteenth century many men as well as women worked

VIPER'S BUGLOSS (Echium vulgare)
*Furbish showed the lower part o the plant going to seed. "Viper" refers to the shape of the seed,
thought to resemble a snake's head, while "Bugloss" comes from the Greek word for
ox's tongue and describes the leaves' shape and texture.*

under constraints, suffered frustration, and were unable to follow careers they would have preferred.

There is no doubt that the scientifically inclined Davenport would have been happier as a professional botanist than as a businessman, but opportunities to make a living in the sciences were extremely rare when he was growing to manhood. Hundreds of people like him, taking whatever time they could from the demands of professional and family life, made significant contributions to the natural sciences. For his part, Davenport was a fine example of the dedicated amateur botanist.

He and Kate Furbish carried on the sort of friendship that modern high-speed travel and communication have made all but obsolete. Davenport became her long-distance mentor and adviser. The authority of his written

SQUAWROOT (Conopholis americana)
Relatively scarce, this parasite is dependent on the roots of trees, especially oaks.

replies to her many questions was an important element in her development. An equally important element was that as time passed she came to deal with him on equal terms. They were almost exact contemporaries, a man and woman of the world with broad interests in life. To be sure, Kate maintained an elaborate courtesy in their correspondence and frequently deferred to the well-connected gentleman, but she derived the advantages of serious dialogue. They were two experts, respectful of each other's accomplishments, exchanging information and specimens and talking over the knotty problems of their particular science.

Kate's first letter to Davenport, on August 3, 1875, set forth many of the themes that were to dominate their correspondence for three decades. She wrote to him from the family cottage on the shore at Harpswell, near Brunswick, sitting before a bright fire while "a North East storm rages outside." She expressed gratitude, formally yet undoubtedly sincerely. She thanked him for several ferns he had sent her and accepted his offer to send specimens of flowering plants to fill gaps in her collection. She listed by their scientific names several plants she especially desired, including "*Potentilla fructi* — I don't remember the last syllable of the last plant and have no Botany [Gray's *Manual*] here — they are not common with us." It was an unusual lapse on her part, for she usually handled scientific names with ease, perhaps as a dividend from that dollar paid by her father 30 years earlier for a Latin course.

Kate offered to send Davenport specimens of the

unusual ferns she came across in her own exploration. "I have only found 14 new plants since my return," she told him, and then sounded another note that was to become common in her correspondence. "I am hoping to secure 100 new plants this summer — but it looks doubtful now — owing to my feeble health." She attributed her the weakness to overwork during the previous winter, but in their subsequent correspondence she nearly always included some reference to her ill health. She closed with a phrase that was to become familiar: "I inscribe myself your Botanical Friend, Kate Furbish."

The first letter alluded to a long trip she was planning. One of her father's last wishes was that she and John keep an eye on their younger brother Frank, who showed small capacity for managing his own affairs. Frank had drifted to Grand Rapids, Michigan, in search of business opportunities; in the autumn of that year Kate went there by train. Naturally, she hoped to see something of the Michigan countryside, also, but soon after her arrival a horse she was riding suddenly bolted and threw her, breaking her ankle. She was confined for nearly four months to the house where she had gone for a brief visit.

By then it was the end of February 1876, almost time to return to the East. Still determined to see some of the country, Kate accompanied a friend on a three-

BEE BALM (Monarda didyma)
This square-stemmed plant is another member of the mint family. Kate Furbish found it in Fayette.

day trip into Michigan's north woods. "I rode through broken forest for 18 miles and had my sleigh ride of the winter there." Then the indomitable Kate boarded a train to spend the spring with her relatives in Delaware.

"All help me to flowers, but I do not find any thorough botanist here," she wrote to George Davenport from New Castle at the end of April. "I'm indebted to you for many favors, and if I'm not able to repay you in kind, *I will try to keep the stone rolling* by doing someone else a like favor."

Still convalescing, Kate depended on her New Castle friends to scour the nearby fields and woods for the plants she needed to sketch. Apparently, she sketched mainly those that also grew in Maine, practicing for the time when she would collect them on the spot. When Davenport offered to send specimens to her in New Castle, she revealed the range of her quest, which now included trees as well as herbs and shrubs. "You may send me the oak blossoms for I do not find them here," she wrote. "I suppose it will be a difficult thing for me to procure both [male and female] blossoms of many of the trees.... I think it would be best to place them without previous pressing between two pieces of Back-board — instead of packing them in a box — then the foliage would not be likely to wrinkle. I don't know as I can get them sufficiently fresh to use, but I'm anxious to do what I can this year."

65

It was the year of the nation's Centennial, and Kate, patriotic and fascinated by the era's developing technology, delayed her return to Maine to attend the Philadelphia Exposition. Despite a minor train accident and resultant long walk to the gate on her tender ankle, she was on hand for the exposition's opening on May 10, 1876. She returned in June for a tour, which she described in her journal in great detail. "Machinery Hall has more attractions to me than to many ladies for I always enjoyed it," she wrote. She

Kate Furbish, a formal portrait in which is apparent the clear, direct gaze that was characteristic of her through the end of her life.

was curious about the workings of all sorts of machines, such as a Corliss steam engine and elaborate knitting machinery, and about the various steps in cork making, silk manufacture, and the production of collars and cuffs. "It seems wonderful to me that so much can be done by machinery," she wrote. On July 7 she returned to Brunswick after an absence of nearly nine months.

Kennebec and Androscoggin counties are named for the splendid rivers that flow through them before uniting in Merrymeeting Bay. The counties occupy a broad, hilly transition zone west of the Penobscot River where the great hardwood forests of the central and northern United States meet the spruces and firs of Canada.

Mingling with the beech, maples, and other hardwoods of this part of Maine is the eastern white pine *(Pinus strobus)*, whose cone and tassel form the state's floral emblem. The tree was the basis of Maine's most important industry, wood and wood products, though much of the accessible virgin pine had been cut before Kate Furbish's time. Yet even today, as one drives north from Brunswick into the interior counties, the rural

areas look much as they did a century ago — narrow roads winding over hills and past stone walls and cattail marshes, with a few tall, ancient pines standing as reminders of the lumbering era.

Now Kate was doing serious botanical work. For the first few years, she had done most of her collecting in the vicinity of Brunswick. (She noted later with a touch of pride that in two seasons she obtained and sketched 275 plants in the area, 50 more than in the regional checklist compiled by a Bowdoin College professor.) But after returning in 1876 as a purposeful, independent woman, she began to map out her campaign to prepare a Maine flora — a major work on the plants of the state. She would survey the state county by county and, almost like a military tactician, mount an assault on each in turn.

In early October of 1876 she was at Fayette Ridge in Kennebec County. In a letter to George Davenport she remarked that two of his letters had arrived in the same post because in that remote place the mail was usually delivered only once a week. She was absorbed in sketching conifers. "I know that it is long past July when Dr. Goodale advised me to paint the coniferous plants, but I've been able all along to find fresh specimens. So as regards Abies alba [then the name for white spruce, now *Picea glauca,*] *please* give up [looking for it], and if I do not find it here I'll give it up 'till another year, when (D.V.) [God willing] I shall secure a person to climb for me for the season as I need. The trouble with those whom I know is they never learned to climb."

PLUMELESS THISTLE (Carduus acanthoides)
*This Europeon species occurs in Maine only in Kennebec County, where
it was found by the artist in a swamp at Fayette on July 4, 1894.*

Although it was her aim to complete most of her plants in watercolors, she portrayed the conifers in black and white. "I am finishing my sketches of these in neutral tint," she told Davenport. "I *hope* they resemble engravings." She felt satisfied that she had secured specimens, including the flower and fruit, of two-thirds of all the conifers growing in the state — good work for a brief collecting season. She planned to complete the sketches during the winter and mount the specimens on herbarium sheets. Her decision to render the conifers in black and white proved remarkably appropriate. By graying in parts of the sketches, she produced finished portraits that would have gained nothing from color.

Curiously, when she made her paintings of the hardwood trees, she seldom finished painting the foliage. For many of the oaks, for example, she painted the flowering parts and fruit, but if she touched the foliage

67

AMERICAN CHESTNUT (Castanea dentata)
*Nearly wiped out by a blight in this century, it was collected by the artist at a number
of locations where "all of these trees were growing with forest trees." No more.*

at all it was merely to suggest the oaks' mature color on one or two sketched leaves. Sometimes an individual specimen tempted her to do more, as when she noted of a white oak *(Quercus alba),* "The young foliage of this tree is very beautiful. I hope to color it."

Another tree that she found growing with other hardwoods on Fayette Ridge and portrayed in a finished painting, with a kind of prescience, was the American chestnut *(Castanea dentata).* At the time the chestnut was one of the largest and most common trees in the eastern United States. Nearby on the same ridge she made one of her most interesting discoveries. On her painting of the flowering dogwood she noted: "This is my only station for this plant. It was growing on a rocky wooded hill by a brook."

For the next several summers Kate Furbish would return to the inland rural areas of Kennebec, Androscoggin, Franklin, and Oxford counties, generally boarding with local families. Farmers and loggers often directed her to the location of prospective specimens.

The tendency of some species to put forth flowers before leaves, or to bear only male flowers or female flowers on an individual plant, caused problems for her when she attempted to assemble all the elements of a plant for its portrait. It took time to finish painting all the conifers because for some species she did not have both sterile and fertile flowers from the same tree. Thus, collecting was not simply a random exercise, but one requiring knowledge of where to find the needed

68

FLOWERING DOGWOOD (Cornus florida)
Kate Furbish found this specimen growing on a rocky hill by a brook along Fayette Ridge in 1874.
It was her only "station" for this plant and only the second ever found in Maine.

plants at the appropriate stages of their growth. It could be an arduous and even disheartening business, as she indicated in a note to George Davenport from Farmington. "Yesterday I paid $1.50 for a team. Rode and traveled in woods (time gone 7 hours) in the hot sun and did not get one thing and when I got back my blood boiled, almost, I trembled and felt half dead. Said to myself I'll never be such a fool again — but this morn, my courage is just as good as ever. So changeable are we."

As the summer of 1876 waned, the asters and goldenrods took over the fields and roadsides. These plants, belonging to the composite or daisy family, pose many problems even for professional botanists. At least sixty-five species and subspecies of asters alone are recorded in Maine. Kate Furbish collected twenty-five species, some of them so difficult to sort out that she had to send them to Davenport or the Harvard Herbarium for help in their identification.

She and Davenport exchanged plants at a furious rate. In late summer of 1877 she noted that she had received eighty-eight specimens for her list from her friend in Medford that year, and added: "In my great haste I forgot to tell you that I shall remain one week longer [in Livermore Falls]. Cannot remain longer on account of my journey...then Botany, Goodbye for '77! A short season but I feel every day as though I am painting with my blood."

In September she traveled to Montreal and Quebec for several weeks. In later winter there was the usual sojourn in Boston, where she had an opportunity to see Davenport and other friends at Horticultural Hall.

For all the advantages of independence, Kate was still prey to the insecurity and anxiety of a woman working in comparative isolation. "I should get discouraged sometimes if there was no Mr. Davenport or Miss [Anne] Jackson," she wrote to Davenport. "I do as it is occasionally." She constantly referred to her uncertain health. "No, my health is not better, only as I rest," she wrote to him from Farmington in June 1878. "I'm not working hard but I neither study or read, and write just as little as I can." And again, "I

NARROW-LEAVED GENTIAN (Gentiana linearis)
Another late-blooming plant, the tips of its flower lobes often bend inward.

hope you do not think I have forgotten you altogether for I have not, and my sick head is one excuse."

Another source of anxiety was the matter of her position in the science with which she hoped to be identified. She was quick to suspect an affront. Davenport, who published regularly and was at the center of botanical activity, corresponded and exchanged plants with other botanists all over the country. He put Kate in touch with some of these people, but she was often uncomfortable in her dealings with them. When she did not hear from a collector whom Davenport had suggested might help her with desired specimens, she was embarrassed. "I wish I had never written him," she told Davenport, "*but* I did need the Loblolly Pine to complete the Conifers." And of another botanist with whom she had had some correspondence, she wrote: "*I think* he is one of those men, who *if* I was *young* and the bloom was on the peach, would feel *more interested* in helping me. I tried to show my appreciation by sending him my best work [a painting of trilliums] but I'm not going to wail over it all. For *my* part I help *everyone* whom I can and put my self out to do it too."

Later in 1878 there were more serious problems. Fifteen years earlier her brother John had been unable to rescue their brother Edward from drowning in the Androscoggin River. In August of 1878, John's son Edward, for whom he had had the highest hopes, drowned while swimming at nearly the same place in the river. The boy's death badly shook the family.

Apparently Kate's brother Frank was going through another of his financial crises, for later in the same year she went to Grand Rapids to spend some time with him. As Christmas approached, her thoughts were still on botany. In Grand Rapids she bought a large collecting case for half the price she would have paid for one in Boston and then had two pockets added to it to hold ferns and grasses. Meanwhile, she was about to mail a present to the one botanical friend in whom she had perfect trust, George Davenport. She wrote to him on December 20: "I have copied my new sketch of gentians for you which has *two more* buds on it and is truer in color than the one you have seen. I sketched it

FRINGED GENTIAN (Gentiana crinita)
Kate Furbish painted this flower, which appears in late September, for several of her friends, including George Davenport.

71

A late stereoptican view of Kate Furbish in the bedroom-studio at Lincoln Street, surrounded by religious articles, plant specimens, and sketches — symbols of the concerns that absorbed her throughout her life

for Summer-Fall [gentians blossom late in summer], but did not finish it. Now I have made a better sketch by adding a bud. I *do* hope it is all you can wish for in a 'Blue Gentian.'"

Despite the role Kate often played of student to teacher in her correspondence with Davenport, she also gave advice and encouragement, and he seems to have treated her as a scientific colleague. When he was depressed, she offered him solace. "Work into your science as far as you can. Do everything which is modest to call the attention of the public to your knowledge — you have no more right to place yourself under a bushel.... this work will help make you happy — won't it?

Doesn't it? I've no paper or would rattle over another sheet."

About his proposed publication on ferns she was more specific. "I *would* prepare that *Hand-Book*, by *all means* — put it up cheap. I'll venture it would be a good thing pecuniarily — if cheap.... I'd make it strictly scientific with no flowery sentences — which, though beautiful in themselves, always mar a work in the eyes of *Scientific Men.*"

By 1880 Kate Furbish had put many of her anxieties behind her. Encouraged by Davenport and Anne Jackson, she had come to believe in the worth of her own work. She had always held strong opinions; now, as she surveyed her situation, she found justification for her friends' approval. Her own Flora, which she conceived of as volumes of paintings rather than of pressed plants like Aaron Young's single volume, was taking shape. Her volume on tree blossoms neared completion, with sixty-eight plants on paper and only three more needed. She was having them bound in "very handsome" English calf.

Her collection of other plants was mounting. She could not help comparing her work to George Goodale's collection, which she referred to as "that incomplete 'Portland Catalogue.'"

She worked steadily on her paintings. Her medium was a water-based paint, the pigment suspended in gum arabic, which imparted a kind of sheen to some of the plants. She achieved her light effects by allowing the background to show through. The quality of the paper played a part in producing the desired effect. Apparently she would have preferred to use fine European paper, but did not always have it; whether for economic or other reasons is unclear.

The inadequacy of her paper bothered her. Almost from the beginning she wanted to make it plain to her audience of the future where the blame lay for defects that would show up in her work. As early as 1870, in a painting of partridgeberry *(Mitchella repens)*, she sounded a note of exasperation at the bottom of the sheet: "American paper!" Four years later, at the bottom of her painting of the American aspen *(Populus tremuloides)*, she was sarcastic: "I *adore* this American paper." In 1877, below a barberry *(Berberis vulgaris)*, which was already spotted and fuzzed, she exclaimed in frustration, "Oh! This American paper!" Similar irritable comments appeared at intervals until 1880, when, on a painting of *Aster acuminatus*, no Victorian proprieties could restrain her outburst: "Oh, damn this paper!"

In Boston that January, her confidence received another lift, which she reported to Davenport. "I was much gratified when I saw some plates of the work that is being published at Harvard to find that my corresponding sheets are not inferior. There would be poor encouragement for me to publish, for the printers make such sad work of the colors. I know that you will be glad that mine are as good, and *as* glad as I am to see your valuable work and services appreciated."

Kate even expressed an optimistic note, unique in her correspondence with Davenport, about the state of her health. "My interest has survived," she told him. "I suppose it is because my health is so good, for me, this winter." She went on to outline her plans for the summer. Although she had decided to postpone a proposed trip to Mount Katahdin for another year, she would botanize in Kennebec and Androscoggin counties for three weeks in May, then spend a month in Orono, and from there go on to what must have seemed a frontier — Aroostook County. She exulted, "How soon Spring will be upon those who live to see it!"

HIGHBUSH CRANBERRY (Viburnum trilobum)

It is not related to the cranberries, although it has been cooked as a substitute.
The large outer flowers in each cluster are neutral, lacking stamens or pistils.

Discovery

To a drawing of American beech with some curious shredded leaves that she had collected in 1877, Kate Furbish added an explanatory comment. "An unusual form of *Fagus ferruginea* [now *F. grandifolia*] which I noticed on a tree as I was passing through a large Beech growth in Chesterville. Dr. Asa Gray wrote me that he feared that he should have been skeptical had the plain leaf not been attached."

Her note is revealing. It shows that the amateur botanist from Maine was in direct contact with the dominant figure in her science; further, that she was acquiring the alertness and confidence to detect minor variations in the field and draw interested responses from him. She had come to the notice of eminent botanists and was qualified to make significant contributions of her own.

Her correspondence shows that she read considerably in botanical and other natural history publications. She was, in particular, familiar with the publications of George Goodale, including not only *The Portland Catalogue of Maine Plants* but the report of the survey he carried out in Aroostook County for the Maine Board of Agriculture in 1861 and 1862.

In that report Goodale painted an alluring picture of a sparsely settled and largely unexplored land. During the 1830s this region had been the center of a boundary dispute with Canada — the so-called Aroostook War — which had nearly erupted into a full-scale conflict between the United States and Canada until calmer voices prevailed. Once the dispute was settled, the region became organized as Maine's largest county.

Aroostook County's northern and eastern margins along the Canadian border are especially interesting to botanists. In the far north the Allagash and Saint John rivers flow through regions with underlying slate and sandstone; farther south, to the west of the Saint John, the underlying limestone has helped to create ideal conditions for growing potatoes. Goodale suggested that the special soils and northern latitude would make further exploration rewarding to the botanist. Reading his report with her Maine Flora in mind, Kate Furbish was understandably excited about traveling in "the Aroostook" as a pioneering botanist who might add new species to the state list.

She did not spare herself as warm weather arrived in 1880. After several weeks of vigorous botanizing in Maine's southern counties, she set out for Orono, a town a few miles northeast of Bangor. Bangor was the headquarters of the state's lumber industry in its golden age, and Kate looked on the area as the gateway to the

HAREBELL (Campanula rotundifolia)
Kate Furbish took this round-leaved bluebell from the banks of the Aroostook River.
It is usually found on rocky shores or meadows.

promised land of the north woods and "the Aroostook." She explored nearby fields and bogs and met the boy who was to become Asa Gray's successor at Harvard University and the second important botanical colleague of her life. From Orono she apparently went by train to Mattawamkeag and then by stage to Fort Fairfield in eastern Aroostook County.

Bogs had always fascinated Kate Furbish, as they do most botanists. Orchids, sundews, and pitcher plants give these wetlands an exotic air and tempt anyone seriously interested in wild flowers to brave the mosquitoes and the prospect of sinking into hip-deep muck.

"I first turned my attention to the swamps which are not hard to find," she said later in describing her trip. "It is much more diffi-

HOBBLEBUSH (Viburnum alnifolium)
Its drooping branches often take root and trip or "hobble" the unwary hiker in the northern woodlands.

(*Tofieldia glutinosa*), the harebell or bluebell (*Campanula rotundifolia*), and the Huron tansy (*Tanacetum huronense*), which George Goodale had discovered in the county almost twenty years before.

Goodale had traveled mainly by canoe and thus his survey had been confined to a narrow margin of land along the lakes and rivers. Moreover, it had often focused on forest and agricultural species because it was sponsored by the state, and it had been cut short because Aroostook's so-called autumn drought had lowered the water levels in late summer. (This region receives less rainfall than any other part of Maine.)

Kate Furbish traveled by stage and saw more of the country away from the rivers. She was disappointed in the plants on the roadsides, dismissing them as only "the most common and coarsest

cult to make one's way into these interminable bogs with a comfortable assurance of ever getting out (the stories about men who have gone into these swamps and never been seen afterward, would deter the timid from making the venture), but I found no skeletons, had no misgivings, and always enjoyed surmounting every obstacle which presented itself."

Kate remained in Fort Fairfield for six weeks. Besides the bogs, she explored the banks of the Aroostook River, delighting in finding plants that were new to her and sketching them all. Among those were the smooth wild rose (*Rosa blanda*), the sticky tofieldia

weeds." But by the road that runs along the Aroostook River to Caribou she explored the "Bog on the Barren" and later the almost equally damp and mossy virgin forests. "A hunter told me that he was never dry shod. The unbroken forests do not yield many plants. I have spent weeks in fruitless search for them, with no other reward than the satisfaction of knowing that I had been over the ground, had felt the oppressive silence, had communed with Nature, and though in pursuit of flowers, had been impressed with the grandeur of the forests."

From Caribou, Kate traveled twenty-two miles

GRASS-OF-PARNASSUS (Parnassia glauca)
*Rare in Maine, the water-loving species was collected
by Kate Furbish in Aroostook County.*

directly north to Van Buren and the discovery that has carried her name into another century. At this town, which was then the center of the Maine lumbering industry and the scene of some of the great spring log drives, when logs were floated downstream to the sawmills, she saw the Saint John River for the first time. It is one of Maine's grandest waterways, sweeping in a long arc across the northern part of the state, receiving the lively waters of the Allagash at the town of that name, and forming the boundary between the United States and Canada before winding off into New Brunswick at Hamlin. The Saint John Valley was largely settled by French-Canadians called Acadians, who helped to develop its potato and lumbering industries. The underlying sandstone and slate along the riverbanks produced an unusual flora, as Goodale had realized.

Upon her arrival in Van Buren in August, Kate Furbish went right to those riverbanks. Growing in rocky crevices along the river were tiny plants that she had found elsewhere in Aroostook but that were unusual enough to delight her whenever she came upon them. There were the dwarf Canadian primrose (*Primula mistassinica*), the sticky tofieldia (*Tofieldia glutinosa*), and the Kalm's lobelia (*Lobelia kalmii*). She also found a number of asters, including a new variety of *Aster cordifolius* that was to figure prominently in her life some years later.

She clambered over banks rising steeply from the river, among green alders (*Alnus crispa*), where much of the soil was dampened by water trickling down from meadows above. Near the alders she noticed a small stand of plants with dull yellow corollas and fernlike leaves. A casual botanizer might have passed them by after dismissing them as the common lousewort (*Pedicularis canadensis*), a plant familiar in most of the eastern United States (though unknown in Aroostook County). Louseworts of several kinds have been known for centuries in both Europe and North America. They are members of the snapdragon family, the Scrophulariaceae. The name is an outgrowth of an old belief that cattle feeding where louseworts grew somehow became infested with lice.

COMMON LOUSEWORT (Pedicularis canadensis)
This species, to which the Furbish's lousewort is related, is also called the wood betony.

When Kate bent to examine the plants, she realized that they were a kind she had never seen before. She collected several of them, roots and all, and put them in her vasculum, or collecting case, for further study. It seems that she guessed from the beginning that she had found a plant new to science.

Charles D. Richards, emeritus professor of botany at the University of Maine, has described the plant that she discovered: "It is an herbaceous plant with deeply cut, fern-like leaves arranged alternately on the stem. The upper leaves are normally smaller than the lower ones and are less deeply cut. The flowers are borne in a bead-like cluster at the tip of the stem and its branches. They have a two-lipped, yellow corolla, and each flower is surrounded by several green bracts. The plant may be found in flower anywhere from the middle of July to the end of August."

This lousewort has been found nowhere in the world except along a 130-mile stretch of the Saint John River, from Andover, New Brunswick, to a point just upstream from its confluence with the Big Black River. The plant's special needs for growth are only partly understood, but its environment never varies appreciably from the site in Van Buren where Kate Furbish

FURBISH'S LOUSEWORT (Pedicularis furbishiae)
*This wild snapdragon, collected by Kate Furbish at Van Buren on the banks
of the Saint John River in August 1880, helped her name endure.*

discovered the original stand. It usually grows on north-facing slopes — often shaded by spruces growing on high land above and partly obscured, though not overwhelmed, by surrounding alders. Richards, one of the few botanists to have investigated the lousewort's ecology, has pointed out its partial dependence on alders.

"The Saint John creates a special habitat," said Richards. "There is a great rise in the river's water level in spring after the snow melts. The water rises up over the banks, and the ice that is carried in its flow clips back many of the alders. If this did not happen, the alders would soon take over the bank and completely shade out the lousewort. Other lousewort species are known to be hemiparasitic, taking some of their food from the roots of nearby plants. It is possible that this lousewort takes some of its food from the alders, because the riverbanks there are very low in nitrogen — and alders possess nitrogen-fixing bacteria in their roots."

It seems poetic justice that a woman who had laboriously built her idiosyncratic life from family loyalty and the few scientific and artistic possibilities available to her was the discoverer of a plant that had evolved a most idiosyncratic life of its own. Unimposing in appearance, thriving only in a very special habitat, and likely to be overlooked, this lousewort resembles the botanist who found it. Plant and botanist seem uncannily linked.

But in 1880 the discovery of the lousewort was a single incident in a great adventure. Kate Furbish pushed on toward Fort Kent, noting that the Saint John increased in beauty as she ascended it. She found Fort Kent rich in wild flowers and hospitable people. "The swamps there are quite accessible, they are not so full of fallen trees over which one must continually climb or else crawl under (to be covered with mud) as in some localities. But those who visit such places in the spirit of which animates an earnest botanist (let all others keep out of them) find their way out of the worst swamps safe, though not always quite as sound as they would like to be, but feeling well paid for all the trouble and

FIREWEED (Epilobium angustifolium)
Named for its habit of growing in burned or cutover places. "I hope to make another sketch, but I doubt it," the artist wrote on it in 1910.

not remembering tumble or scratch. I could spend years in this vast wilderness with entire satisfaction and content. Every morning so fresh, and just as sweet at night."

A single summer was not enough to satisfy Kate Furbish's desire for Aroostook plants. During 1880 she noted 208 species, 50 of them new to her list. She resolved to return the following year.

In 1881 she made sure to arrive during the first week of June to find in flower the plants that she had found before only in fruit. On the first trip she had explored the county's eastern sections — those areas that were centers of potato farming. On the second trip she trav-

ALTERNATE-LEAVED DOGWOOD (Cornus alternifolia)
A northern shrub or small tree, it is far more common in Maine than its relative, the flowering dogwood.

eled through the less populated western region. The journey was arduous and made mostly in a mail stage, an open wagon with no springs or backs to the seats. Accompanied by a friend whom she identified only as a westerner, she traveled directly north from Mattawamkeag to Patten and then on to Ashland.

The country was a vast wilderness. The driver of the stage said that there probably were no houses west of the road until one reached Canada. The road itself was alarming because recent "repair" work had left ditches as deep as ravines on both sides. There were fine views of Mount Katahdin, and long stretches through dense forests where silence itself seemed the only presence. Occasionally they passed empty cabins where lumbermen lived in the winter; the only practical way to get logs out of the muck of the interior was by sled once

the ground froze and was covered by snow. At one point they passed the still smoldering remnants of an enormous forest. It had been burned, according to the driver, by careless hunters.

Kate and her friend spent a week each in Patten and Ashland, collecting and painting. They spent a day at Portage Lake, a well-known backcountry resort for fishermen. "We gathered some Potamogetons [pondweeds] of great size," she wrote afterward, "but they were not in flower, and the day was productive of pleasure alone." Then on they went over the corduroy road toward Eagle Lake.

Kate, in her lectures and articles, knew how to present an image of herself as a field botanist and took advantage of unexpected incidents to dramatize her self-portrait. She wrote about this trip in an article in the *American Naturalist*.

No part of the journey furnished excitement until the driver took his pistol out to load it, saying that he should have done so before starting; that he had been fired upon twice in two years and might need to use it before reaching Fort Kent. He also stated that a peddler who had left this place by that road was never heard from and that his bones were probably bleaching in the woods somewhere. Although we were on the qui vive all the afternoon, we only saw the enemy, for whom he was prepared, quietly standing in their doorways looking as demure as possible.

The people of Fort Kent seem to have welcomed

BONESET (Eupatorium perfoliatum)
The wrinkled leaves unite at their base around the stem.

BUTTONBUSH (Cephalanthus occidentalis)
*Kate Furbish would have detected the jasmine-like fragrance of this
small shrub along the streams and swamps of Aroostook County.*

Kate back as an old friend, for she repeatedly wrote in admiring terms about their good nature and hospitality. Apparently there were no dour Yankees in Fort Kent. Nor were there any complaints from Kate about other obnoxious creatures, for she left no word about Aroostook's insects, and there are no poisonous snakes anywhere in Maine. She reveled, though, in the abundance of wild flowers. A local man brought her a fine specimen of *Clematis verticillaris* which she painted for the first time. In a remote meadow near the Saint John River she found a beautiful gentian (*Gentiana andrewsii*) almost hidden in the lush grass — the first specimen she had seen in Maine.

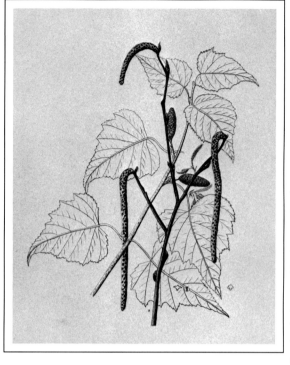

GRAY BIRCH (Betula populifolia)
The specific name alludes to the characteristic of the leaves, which, on their slender stems, tremble in the faintest breeze like those of the poplar.

Sometimes she made discoveries of scientific interest: "A trailing form of *Prunus pumila* [a cherry] grows in large mats in the sand on these Northern rivers, and is decidedly different in its habits from the typical plant. It is always prostrate and very woody, the old wood is often several inches in diameter and of a deep orange color. The fruit is abundant and palatable. I took my specimen to Harvard College Herbarium, and found some *depressed* forms like my own which were gathered at Lake Superior."

When George Goodale visited the Saint John valley twenty years earlier, the local people referred to him and his companions as the "Posy-Men." Now these Acadians affectionately called Kate Furbish the "Posy-Lady." The name stuck.

Although the work that Kate Furbish did in Aroostook County stands as a unified whole at this distance, her two trips were separated by a significant, encouraging event. The travel had fired her imagination so that making flower portraits was no longer enough. Until then, she had confined her writing to an extensive correspondence with friends, relatives, fellow botanists and, during extensive traveling, her journal. Now she wanted a wide audience for the story of her Aroostook adventure. Accordingly, she described her trip in the first of two articles that appeared in the *American Naturalist,* a publication that was by no means restricted to botanical subjects. Additionally, Aroostook served as the focus of a lecture she delivered to the Portland Society of Natural History.

Her *American Naturalist* articles were written in an expansive mood. She was scientific in her account of plant species and varieties encountered, and nearly lyrical in describing the people and landscape. Strangely, her reference to the lousewort was almost casual. After a vivid and rather detailed account of wandering into a stand of giant asters of the common species *Aster puniceus,* but taller than the size limit given by Asa Gray's *Manual,* she noted:

At Van Buren we struck the St. John river, but the same plants which I have enumerated above repeated themselves with a few additional ones. Pedicularis, n. sp.? [new species?] grew three feet high on the bank of the river where the water trickled down its sides.

That was all there was to the description of her discovery of the lousewort. It was as if she were reluctant to mention the possibility of having performed the supremely creative act of adding a new species of organism to the world's knowledge. Yet the thought was much on her mind. She had painted the plant (page 80), had sent a specimen to the herbarium at Harvard for an official description, and then saw to it that her interest in the matter was not forgotten.

It sometimes happens that new species are collected but, not being recognized as such, lie about for years in museums or herbaria with extraneous material. That is what had happened in the case of the new lousewort, for in 1878 and 1879 three specimens of the plant had been taken by Canadian collectors who apparently had no idea of its uniqueness. Those specimens were simply filed away in local herbaria for some years before being identified correctly. There was no such mystery about the significance of Kate Furbish's specimen. Sharp-eyed Kate, knowing at once that she had something special, brought the plant to the attention of the appropriate experts at Harvard.

Then she went further. On January 30, 1881, she wrote to George Davenport from East Livermore, saying: "I shall take the liberty to send the sketches which I made of those Asters, and the Pedicularis.... If Pedicularis sh'd prove to be an unknown species couldn't it be named for the finder, with propriety?"

Here was a plea from a friend and colleague — a plea that Davenport could not ignore. An amateur botanist had made a contribution to the science. He saw an opportunity to recognize in an appropriate way the contributions of all amateurs, for he was in a position to act on Kate's behalf.

Davenport had been in touch with Sereno Watson, a close associate of Asa Gray's at the herbarium and the author of a monograph on North American roses. Watson had examined the lousewort and confirmed that it was a new species. He was preparing to publish a description of the plant for the botanical world and to give it a name. One-half of the plant's scientific name was already determined. It showed close affinities to the various louseworts in the genus *Pedicularis*, and clearly was to be classified with them.

The museum expert who officially describes a new species selects a specific epithet for the second part of its scientific name. This word generally refers to one of

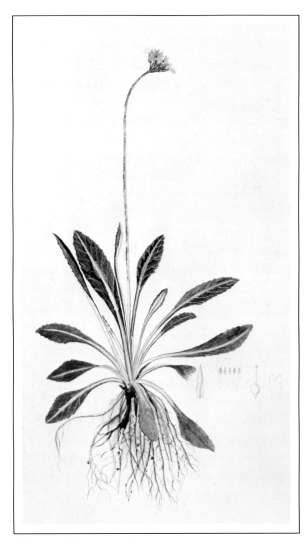

BIRD'S-EYE PRIMROSE (Primula laurentiana)
A yellow eye and notched petals are helpful diagnostic marks of this plant that Kate Furbish collected at Houlton.

the plant's physical characteristics, its finder or another person to be honored, or the locality in which it was discovered. The specific epithet of *Tofieldia glutinosa*, for instance, refers to the sticky substance invariably found on its stem. *Lobelia kalmii* is named for Peter Kalm, the eighteenth-century explorer of North America. *Rosa virginiana* is named for the locality with which it was first associated.

In 1881 some botanists thought that the use of people's names in botanical nomenclature had been overdone because names had been applied out of friendship or flattery, even though the bearers of those names had no relation to the plants. Sereno Watson was apparently thinking along those lines, for he had decided to name the lousewort *Pedicularis Johanensis* for the Saint John River where it had been found. (At that time it was the custom to capitalize the first letter of a plant's specific epithet if it referred to a person or place.)

Davenport wrote to Watson on March 23, 1881, under the official letterhead of the Middlesex Scientific Field Club:

Thanks for all your kindness, but I am a little disappointed in the name of the Pedicularis. *I was hoping that you would name it for the finder, if new. Miss Furbish will have done so much for the Maine Flora when her work is completed — a work of love carried on year after year with no thought of any return — that the dedication of this new species to her would have been a well merited compliment. Is it too late, or will you consider it impertinent for me to suggest such a change? I will delay writing to her until I have your reply.*

Watson was swayed, and Davenport followed up three days later:

I fear that I may have seemed to ask too much, but I looked at the matter in this way. Miss Furbish has devoted all of her leisure time for a number of years to illustrating the Maine Flora by a series of plates carefully drawn and colored directly from the plants themselves; and now has upward of 800 plates finished.

The work is one of unusual excellence — some of the plates, especially the orchids and willows, which I wish you could see, are marvels of accurate coloring and fidelity — and one of which any state might feel proud. I have long regarded it as worthy of some special recognition, and as Miss Furbish has added to the Maine Flora several plants not in the manual, among others the pretty little Odontites rubra *[red bartsia, now* O. serotina]*, the finding of a new species by her seemed to offer a favorable opportunity to recognize her work by dedicating the plant to her.*

I know it will be to her a pleasant surprise, and encourage her in the continuation of her work and perhaps prompt her to place her work finally where it will be of service to botany — as I have many times suggested to her she ought to do. These were the considerations that prompted my action, but for these I would greatly have preferred the other name. I am on principle not much inclined to favor personal names, believing that descriptive or local names should have the preference as a rule, to be departed from only in rare and, as in this case, special instances.

There are now nearly four million sheets in the Gray Herbarium, kept in compartments in metal cabinets. They constitute a magnificent collection of plants that are available for study by botanists from all over the world. Affixed to one of these sheets is the type specimen of the lousewort — the very plant collected by Kate Furbish in 1880 and described by Sereno Watson. On the sheet is the original identification, *Pedicularis Johanensis*, referring to the Saint John River. But that specific epithet has been crossed out. Under it, in Watson's hand, appears the name *Furbishiae* — Furbish's lousewort.

PURPLE FRINGED ORCHIS (Platanthera fimbriata)
This many-flowered orchid, whose large lower leaves give way to
smaller upper ones, grows throughout Maine.

Grand Tour

Throughout Kate Furbish's life, spurts of furious activity alternated with what might best be called resting stages — periods when her attention abruptly shifted elsewhere or turned inward on private concerns. Now, at the height of her powers and with her life barely half over, there was an eruption of enthusiastic communication and self-revelation — and then silence.

On April 2 of 1883, Kate gave a formal address to the members of the Portland Society of Natural History. Her talk's title, "An Evening in the Maine Woods," was deceptively tame, suggesting merely a half-hour's entertainment before the serving of cakes and tea. Of course, she made references to adventures in the woods and the healing powers of nature, standard fare of the time, but she also made observations and comments that showed the extent to which she had mastered her science. It was a serious lecture on a plane with those of George Goodale and other botanists that she had attended in Boston years before, and it exists in print.

The lecture was in part a summing up. Kate looked back on a decade of serious collecting during which she had gathered more than a thousand species of plants (a century later the complete checklist of vascular plants in Maine totals 2,137 species). Of these she had

sketched about 850; the rest were ferns and grasses, which she had simply dried and mounted. She had donated many of her most valuable specimens to colleges in the Northeast and distributed others to help fill out the private collections of fellow botanists.

Her address described the survey of Maine, county by county, which she had begun in 1871. Still dazzled by her Aroostook experience, she gave over the entire middle part of the lecture to enumerating that county's attractions. As she did so often, she revealed her fascination with watery places. She spoke of trips to ponds in Kennebec County where she first came across the showy lady's slipper (*Cypripedium reginae*) and white fringed orchis (*Habenaria blephariglottis*). She described finding sedges and duckweeds around ponds at Kents Hill and Wayne, and the beautiful seaside mertensia (*Mertensia maritima*) along beaches in York County.

Her flair for the dramatic bursts through in her account of venturing onto Mount Day alone on a cool autumn morning in 1882 after failing to find anyone to accompany her. She made her way up to a wet ravine, abounding in "fine iron pyrites," toward a large pond. A precipitous bank confronted her.

As there was no other alternative I proceeded to

climb it, lifting my basket as high as possible over my head (in it a large hammer, chisel, vasculum, rubbers, insect-net and bottles, and the necessary lunch, besides several pounds of slate-rock gathered for the pyrites). One limb [in those days a lady rarely used the word legs] buried itself at once in the rotten wood, a tree proving a treacherous support, the other was high and dry and the sharp rocks were behind me in the ravine below. I knew not how to extricate myself, and while I stood there studying what to do first, down came the basket with all its contents, striking me on the face and shoulder [and] rattling down into the ravine below. I exclaimed in my despair, Alas! for they were borrowed!

My position was growing painful, so I made a leap as it were for life by throwing as much of my weight as possible on the upper foot, and giving a spring, the earth gave way burying me to my waist; but better this than the other situation. I rested, planned and finally extricated myself, secured the tools, climbed the bank, went on my way, found the pond, brought away a new Sedge, and after eleven hours' absence reached home in safety. The leaves of the Pinus strobus *[eastern white pine] growing about the pond were noticeably long.*

From her arduous field experiences emerged conclusions that she passed on to her audience, as well as to the botanical community. She had come to believe, for instance, that the ranges listed for some plants by professional botanists of the day were arbitrary and occasionally did not conform to natural conditions.

MARSH MARIGOLD (Caltha palustris)
This Old World plant carries with it a handful of damp spongy soil from the edge of ponds or streams where it was found near Brunswick.

Additionally, she suggested that when botanists described a certain plant as "rare," they might have more accurately used the term *local*.

All botanists until recently have looked upon Botrychium simplex *as a very rare fern, but since so many persons have turned to Botany we have it reported from many localities, and generally when found at all it is quite abundant. When we learn to look nearer the ground, I do not believe that we shall hear so much about this species being rare. I gathered upwards of a hundred plants in one spot in Rangeley, varying in height from one to five inches, and twenty-five in Bridgewater. I have mounted seven distinct forms or varieties, which I suppose are only the natural states of development in the growth of the species.*

The subject of variation within species of wild plants greatly interested her. These varieties were among the occasions for her keenest surprise and delight, and she passed on her enthusiasm to the audience through the use of a dozen or more specific examples.

It is said that we see what we look for. An observing person surely sees many things which are not laid down in the Manuals. In Franklin County there were large numbers of Cornus canadensis *[bunchberry] with three whorls of leaves, instead of one, and the flowers deeply tinged with pink. In the same county, I could have gathered hundreds of* Trillium erectum *var.* declinatum *[wake-robin] with purple instead of the usual white flower. I did not find a white one.*

Within weeks after the address, Kate Furbish withdrew almost completely from New England's active botanical community and remained on its fringe for the rest of the decade.

It was a time when a Grand Tour — the grandness depending on the state of one's pocketbook — was obligatory for men and women of sensibility. On June 16, 1883, in an almost symbolic act, Kate set out to put an ocean between herself and Maine by boarding the Anchor Steamship Line's *Circassia* in New York City, outward bound with 154 other first-class passengers for Glasgow. Like many of the others, she was on a ten-week tour called Tourgee's Educational Excursions to Europe, but she planned to extend her time abroad by living for a while in Paris.

As she had done on her other extensive trips outside New England, she kept a detailed journal. She was a more seasoned "journalist" by this time, and her account of the trip flowed more gracefully than had other trip descriptions in the past. She expressed her views of people and events with an almost ironic detachment. From the first day out, she was a traveler at ease in almost every situation. There was little in her writing of the breathless acolyte in awe of the Old World.

The *Circassia*, a 400-foot liner, left New York harbor to meet lively seas head on. The journal's opening lines reflected the thoughts of a veteran, though not quite jaded, traveler who had seen a good many strange sights and was not overwhelmed by the current prospects. This native of the Maine coast, appropriately familiar with nautical terms, commented on the strength of the headwinds as well as the constant shudder of the "screw."

Within a day or two many of her fellow passengers had been laid low by the constant rolling of the ship. The resolute Kate, however, in sometimes less than sprightly condition, made it to the dining room for the appointed four meals a day. "There are many empty chairs at the table," she noted, "but I fill mine." She questioned the chief officer closely and came away with many technical details about the ship and its cargo for her journal, but she relied on her own perceptions to

OXEYE DAISY (Chrysanthemum leucanthemum)
The lyrical scientific name of this species means "golden-flower white-flower," which it is. Kate Furbish would have seen it on her European tour.

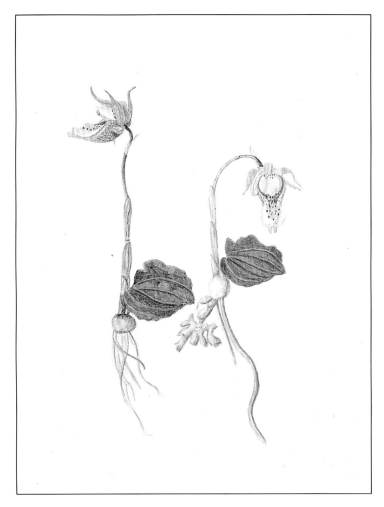

CALYPSO (Calypso bulbosa)
We view this mysterious orchid from two sides.
Rare and reclusive, it grows in only five of Maine's counties.

COMMON SOW THISTLE (Sonchus oleraceus)
*The genus name, meaning hollow, describes the stem, while the common
name comes from the reputed fondness of pigs for its foliage.*

catalog the ship's reigning deity: "The captain is a handsome, surly Englishman, who ought to have his ears boxed." When she was not at table she propped herself in her deck chair and observed the drama of the high Atlantic — porpoises following the ship like cherubs awash, a distant brigantine confronting that vast and hurrying sea, and the dipping and fluttering

Mother Carey's chickens (or storm-petrels), which she described with an ornithologist's attention to detail.

After twelve days the ship reached Glasgow, and Kate Furbish set foot in Europe for the first time. She admired the wild flowers near her hotel in Edinburgh and with the aid of new Scottish friends made a romantic trip in the dead of night to see Sir Walter Scott's

SHEPHERD'S PURSE (Capsella bursa-pastoris)
Its name derives from the triangular seed pods, while the plant itself is often used as a spring green. This is another plant Kate Furbish saw in its Old World setting.

tomb. Then on to London, where this inveterate admirer of churches was spellbound by the splendor of Saint Paul's Cathedral.

Merely getting from one place to another was often an adventure in those days, but the woman who had been through Aroostook County in a buckboard had no qualms about the eleven-hour voyage across the North Sea from London to Rotterdam. She was confined with four other people in a small stateroom, and more than once her journal commented on the readiness of sightseers to put their lives in the hands of strangers. In fact, she showed no patience at any time for the grumblers on her tour.

An aspect of European travel that she found especially attractive was the variety of clothing worn by the peasantry. She collected photographs of washerwomen, fish-women, milkmaids, and other brightly garbed peasants in the lowlands and pasted them in her journal, asserting that she bought only the photographs of actual costumes, churches, and so forth that she had seen in her travels.

On a trip up the Rhine, Kate became positively lyrical. "In the twilight of civilization the ruined castles become the imaginary abodes of spirits," she wrote, "the streams of nymphs; the woods of fairies. It seems but a dream that I am here." On reaching Bavaria she noted that the landscape took on a familiar look. She recognized many of the same wild flowers from home. As they passed some cutover woodlands and roadside lumberyards, several Maine natives in the party exclaimed, "Isn't this like Bangor!"

Italy became the dream of a lifetime realized. There was no note of the jaded traveler here. Kate was enchanted by Venice. Some of her companions, though, wept — not for beauty but because after a long trip they did not get fed. And then there were the ruins of Rome, and Naples with Mount Vesuvius puffing in the background. Going back over the Alps toward Paris, the party just missed an avalanche next to the railroad tracks.

COLTSFOOT (Tussilago farfara)
The shape of the leaves, which do not open until after the flower appears, provide the name for this alien plant.

In Paris Kate Furbish separated herself from the tour. She had been attracted to Montreal and Quebec in past years, and now she apparently wanted to install herself in a situation where she would be able to learn French, see cultural sights, and pursue her studies in painting. At the end of August she moved to a small private hotel that had taken over part of an old palace. She settled in with fourteen other women of almost as many nationalities — students, teachers, and widows for the most part — and began to make the best of her opportunity.

"Books and letters!" she wrote in her journal. "Studying, corresponding, and drawing are my natural ways of having 'a good time.' It was so from childhood and will ever remain so, I presume." She set out to see as much as possible of the city, often wandering the streets alone for hours and returning to the hotel to reflect on the sights.

I have been impressed again to-day with the beauty of the little children, their lovely little faces enveloped in lace and eider-down, showing from their earliest existence the quickness and gayety of the French nature, looking for all the world as though they were taught in a pre-natal state that life was a force, demonstrating to my mind that environment, especially that of the first few years decides the happiness or unhappiness of the whole after life. They do not have the sobriety of old

BUR CUCUMBER (Sicyos angulatus)
The plant's name refers to the fruit, which resembles a tiny cucumber.

age stamped on their faces before care and experience has earned a place there. I think the women fade young, but the men of all classes look as though they were full of life.

Socially, Kate was wary and sometimes weary of the French women of whom she had read so much. Every evening at the hotel the women, both French and foreigners, gathered in the salon for talk and music, but the constant chatter was not to Kate's taste. She often withdrew to the solitude of her room, only to be coaxed back by the proprietor, to whom she had taken an instant liking. Like the other Americans at the hotel, Kate sometimes felt under siege. She left a revealing pic-ture of life in a small Parisian pension a century ago.

The French women at the Pension appear in several dresses during the day; but they are not things of beauty as I had expected from French fashion-plates; but plainly made and exquisite in their fit. The little widow at my right at the table said to me one day, "Mad'selle, you have no good couturieres in America?" I replied we do not lace in A., at least well-bred women do not, when she continued, "French women hate large waists, and think it is very vulgar not to powder, grease is just abominable!" I replied you look old earlier than you would if you did not powder, for it dries the skin to remove the natural moisture which you call "grease"

BLACK HENBANE (Hyoscyamus niger)
The Old World herb contains a poison said to be deadly to fowl, but its leaves yield a medicine once used as a sedative.

by washes and powders. She replied that "men do not care for old women anyway." *Of course, I did not let that go by, and said, ah! so it is men that you* "paint" *and* "powder" *for, is it? Now I understand why we do not — it must be because American gentlemen do not like it. Quick as a thought she found a reason for our not doing it.* "Because American gentlemen do not like it," *and laughed a long ringing laugh.*

The proprietor generally intervened with a kind word for the Americans. Kate found the interplay of nationalities endlessly interesting.

The young girls are very homesick, and I pity them. Only one applied for admission to the Conservatory of Music. It always seemed necessary for Madame [the proprietor] to accompany them there to introduce them, so I asked permission to go and walk back with her. The building is old and seemed uninteresting.

Miss _____ said at the table to-night that she should have no doubt of success at home; but she did not know here. Madame invited her to play in the salon after dinner which she did. I enjoyed it. Mrs. T. of Washington said she played well; but I could see that there were many shoulders raised during her performance. Mrs. Hill of Indiana (who is called "Madame Eel" *here) followed her with songs. She has studied here five years, and sings very acceptably, though I saw two or three shoulders go up. Mrs. McNeil also sang, she is listened to with a good deal of attention; but I do*

ELECAMPANE (Inula helenium)
A large, disheveled plant, it was often found by the artist near old gardens.

not think we could please if we tried....

There was a large party in the salon this evening, and the coal in the [stove] was bright. I stopped till after tea was served for which I was commended. I am weary to-night. I am striving to accomplish all I can before I go into the Studio. I am contented here and well for me.

The following day, September 25, she was at the Louvre by nine o'clock, wearing a heavy shawl against the chill of the galleries. She wrote of her enthusiasms; she was especially keen on a painting she called *The Burial of Atala*, by Girodet. Following that page in her journal she pasted in photographs of some antique sculptures. Then the journal abruptly broke off and was never resumed.

How long did Kate remain in Paris, and what did she accomplish? There isn't much to go on. Twenty-five years later, in a letter in which she alluded to trips to Michigan and Delaware, she spoke of "a year in Paris," but she did not mention her studies. On the other hand, in an *Appreciation* dedicated to her years later, an old friend, Louise Coburn, wrote, "She once for a short time resided in Paris, where she became a student of French literature, which she has always much enjoyed and reads as easily as English."

The evidence therefore suggests that the itinerant Kate characteristically cut short her stay and returned to New England, probably sometime in 1884. But the mystery does not end there. Her trail fades out almost everywhere. There is no clue to suggest how she passed the next three years, and there are very few for the rest of the decade.

Kate kept no journal, nor has any correspondence turned up for this period. There is a gap in correspondence, even with her faithful colleague George Davenport, until 1891. Her plant collecting records, so diligently kept and so numerous through the late 1870s and early 1880s, ceased for three years and appeared only spottily until 1891. In 1887 she collected specimens at Harpswell, near Brunswick, and during the next few years around Portland and the islands in Casco Bay.

Have the records simply been lost? If the correspondence alone were missing, or if the collecting records had disappeared, loss might be as good a guess as any. But it is unlikely that *all* the pertinent documents could have been lost, and thus the pattern indicates a change in Kate Furbish's life. Perhaps she turned to other pursuits that failed to hold her interest for long. There is always the possibility that her health deteriorated. Historians and biographers have commented on mysterious nervous ailments, some of them obviously stemming from profound changes in the structure of American life, that afflicted many women toward the end of the nineteenth century. Kate Furbish, despite her strenuous life in the outdoors, constantly referred to vague indispositions; they may have taken a more serious, all-absorbing form. In any case, the years of dormancy will remain a mystery unless fresh material written by her own hand is uncovered.

Kate still had a long life and new achievements ahead of her. As she had said to the members of the Portland Society of Natural History in 1883, "Surely inspired by this encouragement, and animated by fresh impulses, I may now go on with greater courage than ever before."

COMMON GROUNDSEL (Senecio vulgaris)
The genus name comes from the Latin senex, "old man," for the silky hairs on the seeds resemble an old man's beard.

LABRADOR TEA (Ledum groenlandicum)
Of this common member of the heath family (with another species to the left) Kate Furbish wrote:
"I hope to make a more representative sketch of this plant."

Master Fernald

"I remember vividly my first acquaintance with Miss Furbish who when I was a very small boy, visited my home in Orono, spending the summer there making drawings of the native plants. I used to watch her by the hour at her painting, and throughout the forty odd years succeeding, kept in close, and in some ways filial, association with her."

These words were written by Merritt Lyndon Fernald, one of America's most accomplished academic botanists, a man who was Kate Furbish's second important scientific friend and in the mid-twentieth century made a complete revision of the book that had played so important a role in her work, Gray's *Manual of Botany*. Fernald was a prodigy, and if Kate Furbish did not instill in him his lifelong love of plants, she certainly provided a model of the dedicated botanist for the impressionable child. He seems never to have forgotten his debt to her.

They got to know each other as early as 1880 in Orono, when Fernald was six years old. Kate was preparing for her first trip to Aroostook County, and Orono served as her base of operations in central Maine. While there, she often visited the home of Merritt Caldwell Fernald and Mary Lovejoy Fernald, parents of the precocious Merritt. The elder Merritt was the second president of the Maine State College of Agriculture and the Mechanic Arts, which later became the University of Maine.

As important as Orono's position as a staging area for Kate was its proximity to sphagnum bogs. The Bangor Bog has been well known to Maine botanists for more than a century; more extensive bogs are scattered across the landscape to the north and east of Bangor. Although these cold-water bogs do not hold a great variety of plants, they are endlessly interesting to botanists, and Kate was much attracted to them. Wearing boots and long skirts, she repeatedly explored the bogs, almost unaware of the water that must have flooded over her boot tops as she sank inches deep into the cushiony peat moss and struggled forward, carrying her botanical gear. She later described those strenuous expeditions.

Few men or women care to endure the fatigue which usually attends such excursions, but a true botanist (what a difference there is between the meaning of the two words "collector" and "botanist") feels richly repaid for it in every way. Strange to say, the inhabitants of these sacred silent places scarcely flutter at your approach, the squirrel sits and gazes at you, scolds perhaps, but does not scamper away; and the cedar-

YELLOW LADY'S SLIPPER (Cypripedium calceolus)
The artist noted that this specimen, collected in Livermore Falls,
is of the variety parviflorum, which is now considered
a separate species and usually found in bogs.

LAMBKILL (Kalmia angustifolia)
The bright flowers cluster at the tip of last year's leaves, the
new leaves growing from the middle of the flower cluster.

CHOKEBERRY (Pyrus arbutifolia)
Chokeberries are often found growing in small colonies at the edges of swamps and bogs.
They help to brighten Maine's spring with their terminal clusters of white blossoms.

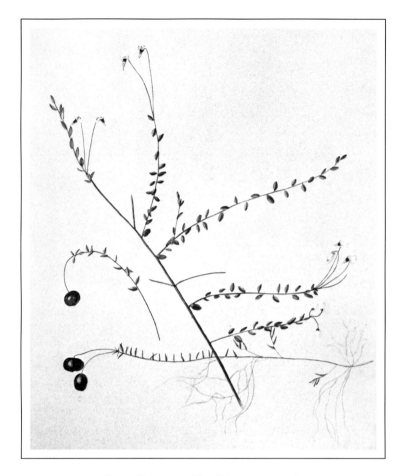

SMALL CRANBERRY (Vaccinium oxycoccus)
The flowers, and later the berries, spring from the tips of the plant's stems.

partridge [spruce grouse] hardly notices your move-ments at all. The dew drops on your hat and shoulders all day, and in hot July when everything outside is dry and parched, and the sand burns your feet, there's no more delightful retreat than one of these damp cool swamps.

A sphagnum bog is a unique ecosystem. It is pro-duced by a succession of plants that occupy a small body of still water. As layer after layer of dead plants gradually accumulate, they eventually fill it up. Layers of sphagnum moss form a dense mat, soggy with acidic, stagnant water, which is poor in minerals and other plant nutrients.

Only a select roster of plants can grow under such conditions, and Kate Furbish did justice to almost all of them. Characteristic of the vegetation is the pitcher plant *(Sarracenia purpurea)*. A most prominent vegeta-tive feature is an array of Ericaceae, or heath plants. But the chief lure of bogs to most botanists is their abun-dance of orchids. In 1883 Kate Furbish reported that she had collected thirty-seven species and two varieties. Because a good many of these orchids had been found during her early explorations of the Bangor Bog, she returned there often in later years and was undoubtedly privy to the event of 1891 in Orono that concerned her young friend, Merritt Lyndon Fernald.

PITCHER PLANT (Sarracenia purpurea)
This Furbish painting of this well-known bog-loving plant was one of the first to be published,
appearing in Louise Coburn's Appreciation *in the 1920s.*

CREEPING SNOWBERRY (Gaultheria hispidula)
The tiny, bell-shaped flowers are pretty, but more people know the
plant from the oval evergreen leaves along creeping stems
and the white berry that tastes of wintergreen.

BOG ROSEMARY (Andromeda glaucophylla)
The narrow leaves are white below, with very fine hairs.

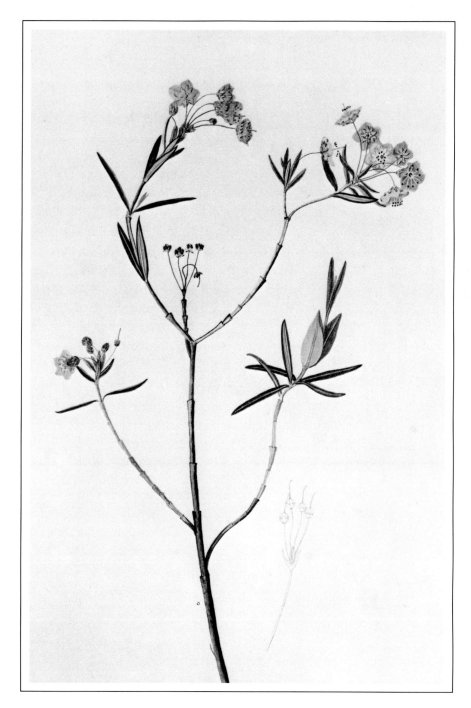

PALE LAUREL (Kalmia polifolia)
The flowers appear at the tip of this branching plant, which grows in both cold bogs and on mountain tops.

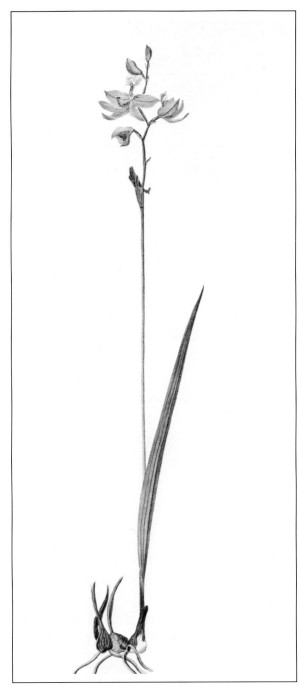

GRASS PINK (Calopogon pulchellus)
The stalk and leaf of this orchid grow from the small bulb pictured here.

For some time Fernald had been in touch with Sereno Watson, the director of the Harvard Herbarium, the man who had formally described and named the Furbish's lousewort. It may have been that Kate herself had put the boy in touch with Watson, though the elder Fernald, a Harvard graduate, had also known Watson while he was in Cambridge. In any case, young Merritt had regularly sent specimens and queries to Watson and received stimulating replies. At the age of sixteen he ventured statements of a highly technical nature, such as his comment, accompanying a specimen of *Juncus*, that he was "more and more convinced that it is not described in the Manual." In February 1891, Watson wrote to the young man and offered him a position in the herbarium. Fernald promptly replied that he was giving the offer careful consideration. "I think the one thing I was made for was a botanist, as from early childhood my inclinations have been in that line.... I know very little about 'Textbook Botany,' my work having been mostly in the field, and should I go to Cambridge, I should want to study as much as possible and do the required work satisfactorily."

His father followed up with a letter accepting the position for young Merritt, with certain conditions. He noted that his son, who was seventeen and a first-year student at the college in Orono, was "an earnest, conscientious, Christian boy" and went on to speak about his and his wife's concern for their son's future.

We have no expectation but that, if spared, he will devote his life to Botany. We have designed, however, that his general culture should be fairly generous also. We can assent to an interruption of his course here provided he can continue, to an extent, his general studies elsewhere. Will it be possible for him to devote a portion of his time to a systematic course of study either under a private tutor or as a special student in the University while attending to work in the Herbarium? We should be content for him to do this general work slowly, but deem it essential that it be done.

The arrangements were speedily concluded, and in early March the elder Fernald escorted his son on the night train from Bangor to Boston and saw him installed in suitable lodgings near the Harvard Herbarium. When Merritt began his course of study at Harvard University in the fall, his father negotiated with Watson for relatively higher wages to cover the young man's increased expenses. Merritt more than lived up to his early promise, establishing a formidable reputation while still a young man as both a field botanist and a systematist. At first, his elders watched his rapid progress with amused surprise, and Kate Furbish wondered in a letter to Davenport why "Master Fernald" had found several species abundant in Aroostook County where she had not seen them at all.

Meanwhile, Fernald pursued his general studies and in 1897 earned a bachelor of science degree, magna cum laude. It was the only degree he ever earned. Some measure of the eminence he nevertheless achieved may be grasped from the story, perhaps apocryphal, that when asked why he never earned a doctorate, he replied, "But who would examine me?"

From 1891 on, Fernald, from the herbarium, corresponded with Kate Furbish about her investigations and kept in touch with the botanical scene in his native state. Kate found herself in the new role of senior field botanist in this exchange. Respectful of her experience, the young man continued the relationship in that key for the rest of her life.

ARROWHEAD (Sagittaria latifolia)
The leaves of this species of swamps and slow streams vary from broadly arrow-shaped to the slender outline shown in the present painting.

The Collector

The Poland Spring House rose to nationwide fame on the nineteenth century's enthusiasm for therapeutic spring water. Fashionable vacationers "took the waters" at various spas in Europe and America, assuring themselves and each other of the springs' beneficial properties and making household words of such place names as Baden-Baden, Marienbad, and Saratoga Springs. The Poland Spring and the resort that grew up around it in Maine's Androscoggin County attracted the well-to-do from all the large eastern cities and, for a few years, offered Kate Furbish the only professional position of her botanical career.

The site of the Poland Spring House had been acquired by a man named Jabez Ricker in 1794 from the Shaker religious community at nearby Sabbathday Lake. Later, the Shakers, who were dedicated to celibacy, simple food, and the homespun life, must have looked with dismay on the opulent resort that stood on their former land. The development began quietly enough when Ricker took hungry travelers into the house he'd built there for his family. Within a few years he offered meals and lodging on a regular basis. Quite conveniently, his grandson went haying one day and discovered that copious drafts of water from a large

spring on the property cured his "dyspepsia." The word spread abroad, and the rush was on.

The Ricker family eventually built an enormous hotel, rivaling in size any in the world, on a high hill looking west toward the White Mountains, with Mount Washington plain in the distance on fair days. Broad verandas encircled the building; oriental rugs, fine furniture, and white-gloved busboys set the tone inside. Outbuildings included greenhouses for the provision of fresh flowers, extensive stables, and even quarters to house the carriage drivers (later, the chauffeurs) of wealthy guests. Residents of the Shaker community often walked up the big hill to sell their handmade baskets at the hotel and be served tea by the proprietors.

In May 1893, Kate Furbish wrote to her old friend George Davenport from the Poland Spring House. "You will undoubtedly be surprised to know that I have rec'd. the appointment of Botanist to this House for the flowering Season — which will be into Sept. of course. I hope that I shall be well, and that none of the dear ones will need my personal care; for it seems to be an opportunity to improve in health; if the waters are really what they claim to be.... The object of the Messers Ricker in appointing a botanist here is for the amusement of the half invalid — I hope I shall 'fill the bill.'"

Part of Kate's duties was to gather information about the plants of adjacent woods and fields and to prepare a pamphlet on the subject for the hotel's guests. She reported that she was keeping a rudimentary journal, listing the location and flowering dates of the plants in the vicinity, and asked Davenport for advice on drawing up a plan for the pamphlet.

"I have catalogued 103 plants in four days which have peeped out of the ground far enough to be named," she wrote to Davenport. "I am somewhat west of Brunswick but I find the Flora identical so far — only as yet I find no Spruce, Fir, or Saxifrage. Of course the reason that I do not find the trees is because they have been obliterated."

Kate did not mention then or later the terms of her connection with the resort. It is possible that she served as botanist in return only for room and board. At any rate, she felt profitably employed and went about her duties very seriously. In a letter to Davenport she described her life there early in the first season. "I wish my botanical friends could all come here while I am here. There are but few here at present and there are two very sick people here which depresses me, one just opposite me, the cough denotes the end is near. Well, in one way it is a Sanitarium."

Much of Kate Furbish's correspondence in 1893 and the next two years concerned her work at the resort. Sometimes she wrote under the hotel's letterhead — an ornate hodgepodge that covered more than a quarter of the page and featured arabesques of flowers, scenes of the main building and its tree-shaded grounds, a facsimile of the seal affixed to bottles of Poland Spring Water (warning the user to "look out for imitations"), the names of various members of the Ricker family, and the addresses of the company's offices in Boston and New York. Her letters to Davenport were frequently accompanied by specimens of ferns for identification, since she confessed her ignorance of this branch of botany and wanted to avoid mistakes that might be "picked up by Critics."

TURTLEHEAD (Chelone glabra)
While at Poland Spring, Kate Furbish searched for specimens such as this at the edges of ponds and streams.

CARDINAL FLOWER (Lobelia cardinalis)
Growing at the edges of ponds and streams throughout Maine, the blossom provides a double
pleasure for admirers, who may view it from afar, and again reflected in water.

HORNED BLADDERWORT (Utricularia cornuta)
The mud at the edge of ponds and lakes is brightened by
the splash of yellow from this plant's flowers.

Of increasing importance to her was her relationship with Merritt Fernald. Kate had embarked on a project of more significance than the preparation of a pamphlet: she was assembling an herbarium for the Poland Spring House. Far from a collection of mounted plants to be kept in an upstairs room at home, this was to be a formal work put on display for thousands of people at one of the country's outstanding resorts. Determined that the identifications of the species and rare varieties be as accurate as was humanly possible, she sent off packages of grasses and sedges, as well as more familiar plants, for Fernald's authoritative assessment.

Among those specimens was the large whorled pogonia, an orchid that is rare in New England, though fairly common to the south. The plants of this species found by Kate Furbish near the Poland Spring House were the first ever collected in Maine, and since then it has been noted in the state only at a few stations. Fernald had special labels printed for her to use on her mounted specimens. They read: "Flora of Maine — Kate Furbish."

WATER LILY (Nymphaea odorata)
*The sweet-scented flower grows from three to five inches across. Its showy
beauty would have pleased patrons of the Poland Spring House.*

115

GREAT WATER DOCK (Rumex orbiculatus)
The leaves of this plant of wet places may grow to be two feet long.

MONKEY FLOWER (Mimulus ringens)
*The violet tips of this distinctive flower suggest the face of a
mimic or buffoon. One of the many plants of wet
places that the artist loved to paint.*

FLORA OF MAINE.
KATE FURBISH.

No. _____ *Caryophyllaceae.*
Silene Cucubalus, Wibel.
Orono, '91.
South-Poland, '93.
Rangeley, '94.
M. Baldwin. '00.
Legit *Kate Furbish*

These labels would be used again later when she put together her collection of paintings. Meanwhile, they were designed for the mounted specimens, which were to find an unexpected setting at the resort. The Rickers had arranged to have the State of Maine Building at the Chicago World's Fair of 1893 moved to the Poland Spring House. The building was reassembled there and opened as a library in 1895.

Although the Poland Spring House itself burned some years ago, the State of Maine Building still stands on the site. It is an octagon of several tiers built of stone below and wood above, with four turrets and a central tower, or cupola. Kate was proud of this setting for the

HEART-LEAVED ASTER (Aster cordifolius var. furbishiae)
This variety was found by Kate Furbish on both of her trips to Aroostook
County and named in her honor by Merritt Fernald.

herbarium she assembled and took great pains to see that the collection remained intact.

"I often wonder how this set of plants will look to you, one of these days, when you see it in the 'Maine Building' at Poland Spring," she wrote to Fernald. "You will see by the 'mount' and the enclosed sample of 'Genus-Cover,' that I have preserved the best material. Each plant in a Genus-Cover of its own; but there was no other way to *preserve* them; for they would be soon ruined in such a place, where every Mother there, will want her children to see them. I've been there to see what they do."

Meanwhile, she was collecting for Fernald as well as for herself, and sending him packages of plants which he was apparently eager to have. "I have almost taught the science this year," she remarked of the summer of 1895, "and the only questions which I could not answer did not come within my range of work. I would like to ask you the same questions, sometime."

The steady stream of plant specimens sent to Fernald by his friend from Poland Spring was only one of the many ties that bound him to the Maine botanical scene. Through the years Kate Furbish had often referred to the "incomplete Portland Catalogue," and in 1891 the directors of the Portland Society of Natural History asked Fernald to revise completely the work that George Goodale had compiled nearly a quarter century earlier. This was a considerable honor for the eighteen-year-old Fernald, who had just begun his duties at the Harvard Herbarium.

Fernald went right to work on the project, and in 1892 the society published the *Second Edition of the Portland Catalogue of Maine Plants*. In his introduction, Fernald noted the importance of having every botanist working in the state "report the occurrence, within the limits of his observation, both of all plants recorded in this list and especially of those not yet placed there, and which may prove to be new discoveries." He urged botanists to send specimens for positive identifications either to the Portland Museum or to him at the Harvard Herbarium. He concluded by acknowledging the outstanding work of a few Maine

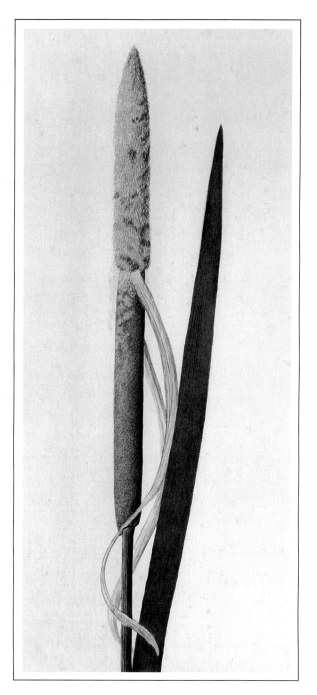

CATTAIL (Typha latifolia)
The head of this marsh plant is packed with tiny pistillate flowers, and the "tail," or upper part, with staminate flowers.

WHORLED POGONIA (Isotria verticillata)
Of this species, which she collected near the Poland Spring House in 1895, Kate Furbish noted, "scarce."
It has not been found recently and may have disappeared from the state.

botanists, including Goodale, Joseph Blake, and Kate Furbish.

Among the additions to the *Catalogue* were two plants named after Kate. One, of course, was the Furbish's lousewort. The other was the variety *furbishiae of Aster cordifolius,* which she had found first in 1880 at Van Buren in Aroostook County.

The last decade of the century was a period of great activity in the botanical exploration of Maine. There had been a surge of interest in the subject in the quarter century since Kate Furbish had set out to paint Maine's flora; by 1895 an estimated 100 collectors (some, summer residents) were adding to the state list. One of these knowledgeable amateurs was Jennie May Morrell of Gardiner, who wrote to Fernald in 1895, suggesting that professionals and amateurs join forces to organize a state botanical club. Fernald replied enthusiastically and arranged to have a letter that would be signed by himself, Mrs. Morrell, Kate Furbish, and other botanists sent to interested people all over the state, inviting them to a five-day convention to open in Portland on July 12.

Kate Furbish left the Poland Spring House for the occasion and joined nearly 100 others at the Portland Museum of Natural History on the appointed day. She gave one of two papers presented at the opening session, talking about the rare and interesting plants of the Poland Spring area. The following day Fernald spoke on a subject of special interest to him, the distribution of Maine plants, and took the leading role in finding a name for the new organization. Some of the participants favored a name that would emphasize the state, such as the Maine Botanical Club. Fernald, however, argued for a more distinctive name. Producing a copy of John Josselyn's first book, *New England's Rarities Discovered in Birds, Beasts, Fishes, Serpents, and Plants of That Country,* he proposed that they honor Maine's earliest botanist. After some discussion, the convention members voted to name the new organization the Josselyn Botanical Society of Maine. Kate Furbish was elected one of its vice-presidents and, along with Fernald, appointed to its committee on plant distribution.

Kate's solitary labors over so many years received further recognition that year when Fernald produced a supplement to the *Second Edition of the Portland Catalogue of Maine Plants.* In it he elaborated on the naming of the variety of *Aster cordifolius* that she had discovered in Aroostook County.

Dedicated to Maine's distinguished artist-botanist, the "posy-lady" of the Madawaska Acadians, who through her undaunted pluck and faithful brush, has done more than any other to make known the wonderful flora of the "Garden of Maine."

MOUNTAIN ASH (Pyrus americana)
*This small tree, whose bright red berries are as attractive as its flat clusters of white flowers,
often grows on rocky ledges near the coast.*

The Shape of Life

On Washington's Birthday, 1896, Kate Furbish wrote to her old friend George Davenport from Brunswick: "I am reminded by this date that winter is fast passing away and that I have accomplished very little. Who does do much now-a-days! In the old times people were content to do well; but this breakneck age places everyone on the shelf who lags at all."

She had passed her 60th birthday two years before and was well established in the botanical community. She was at a time of life when most of her contemporaries were beginning to slow down and rest on their laurels. But she had worked too hard to pull back now, for she may have felt that her identity — Kate Furbish, botanist-painter — was the equivalent of life itself. The literary critic George Steiner has remarked on the uncanny absorption of some people in their subject, in keeping "with Nietzsche's finding that to be interested in something, to be totally interested in it, is a libidinal thrust more powerful than love or hatred, more tenacious than faith or friendship — not infrequently, indeed, more compelling than personal life itself."

More and more, Kate Furbish came to exhibit a single-minded attention to the collection and painting of wild plants. She was determined that society was not going to put her "on the shelf." Therefore, the decade that began with the founding of the Josselyn Society saw a burst of activity nearly the equal of any other period of her life.

Working was undoubtedly difficult. The ailments that sometimes seemed vague in her earlier years now took on formidable dimensions. "Neuralgia" afflicted her hands and feet and seldom gave her a day without pain, so that the very substance of her life — exploring the woods, shores, and bogs, and painting the plants she collected — must have been a torture at times. And occasionally there were bouts of a more crippling nature. One summer, as she reported to Davenport, she was confined to her house and yard for eight weeks with "dropsical limbs," and "we both know that two months taken out of the best of the year cannot be made up to any of us who study plants."

Yet she threw herself into all sorts of projects. For some time Davenport had considered publishing a paper on his beloved ferns; he asked her to provide the illustrations. He sent her photographs of ferns from which she could work, and in her reply she expressed an artist's admiration for the splendid effects that could be achieved in the newer medium. "I cannot see why you do not use the photographs to illustrate your work

GLASSWORT (Salicornia europaea)
A succulent shore plant with jointed stems, it is rich in soda and was once useful in making glass.

with, no hand can be *as absolutely* correct as the sun. The photograph of the larger fern is very beautiful. The tone of the paper very desirable…what kind of paper and pencil do you wish used?"

Kate was in demand to give botanical talks to women's clubs and granges. She went off to visit her relatives in New Castle, Delaware, and made a stopover in New York City. She planned a trip to Bermuda, which she abandoned in the press of botanical business. There were various meetings to attend,

such as that of a federation of natural history clubs in Portland, where she greatly admired the lifelike drawings a Boston biologist had made of spiders ("His water-colors are wonderful, also the action which he has put into the disagreeable things"). And after another visit to Portland she confided to Merritt Fernald that she wished she lived in that city instead of in Brunswick "where I do not get an encouraging word once a year."

She never had any reason to complain of a lack of

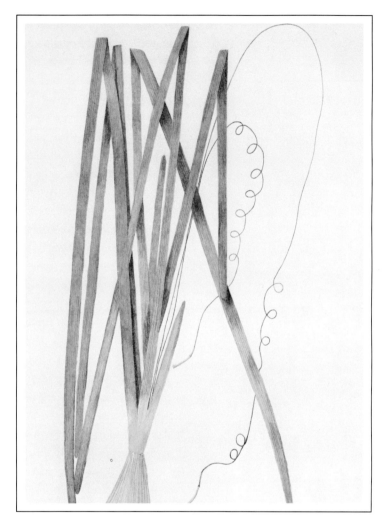

EEL GRASS (Vallisneria americana)
The plant, which has leaves several feet long, grows in brackish coastal waters.

encouragement from Fernald. She was always welcome at the Harvard Herbarium, which she visited on her annual trips to Boston. It was a red-letter day when she saw him, though she realized how busy his increasing duties kept him. She never failed to write him in advance from Malden, or wherever else she was staying, to ask him "to give me a little time."

She read with much interest every issue of the New England Botanical Club's journal *Rhodora*, to which Fernald contributed many scholarly articles and which

he later served as editor. Unlike the Josselyn Botanical Society, this club barred women from membership, and thus Kate Furbish could not take part in its activities. (The club opened its doors to women only when its policy jeopardized its tax-free status in the 1960s, prompting some unrepentant members to resign in protest against the outrage.)

Kate Furbish's ties with the Harvard Herbarium remained strong. Fernald valued her regular contributions of plant specimens, which were added to the

WAX MYRTLE (Myrica pensylvanica)
Kate Furbish said of this shrub, also called Bayberry,
"common on the coast," and it remains so.

growing collection under the herbarium's care. As we have seen, one of Fernald's major interests was the study of plant distribution, and he needed to confirm range extensions, variations, and recent discoveries by obtaining botanical sheets.

In return for the specimens, Kate sought information from Fernald, who was rapidly becoming Asa Gray's successor as the dominant figure in New England botany, about problems she encountered with her collection. Her letters to him are full of botanical shoptalk. She marveled at his ability to distinguish minute variations in the asters she had sent him from her Poland Spring collection. She enclosed a specimen of grass with the notation that a local man had called it goose grass, and she thought that Fernald would want the name because of his interest in folklore. She asked him which edition of Gray's *Manual of Botany* was the more valuable, for she had in her possession one of the earlier ones.

A highlight of any year for her was a visit by Fernald to Brunswick. In December, 1900, she anticipated one such visit. "Now about the '*hour*' which you hope to pass with me during the Holidays. I suppose when you close the Herbarium down for your vacation, you will say to yourself 'good riddance now and for two weeks I will not even *think* of plants.' But I have a plan to propose. I wish it could be agreeable to you to go home and make your visit, then leave there two or three days before you are pledged to Cambridge, and so pass that time with me. I have passed nearly a month in looking through my Herbarium, and although some of the plants are broken and others poorly pressed, I only found nineteen plants which were badly eaten…my mounted specimens as far as I know are not infested. You said to me once that there were some things hidden away which would be 'very interesting.' I am desirous of securing your authority for saving or discarding. I both wish them off my mind, and off my hands where they will do someone some good. What do you think of my plan?"

A subject often on her mind was the progress of the Josselyn Society. In 1896 she accompanied the other

126

HEART-LEAVED ASTER (Aster cordifolius var. polycephalus)
This aster was drawn from a dried plant given to Kate Furbish by her friend Merritt Fernald.

ORACH (Atriplex patula)
*A plant commonly found in salt marshes, and favored by
holiday foragers for the variety it adds to salads.*

members, whom she called "Josses," to the second annual meeting at the Normal School in Farmington, and a year later to Dover-Foxcroft. This Piscataquis County town was the original home of Merritt Fernald's family, and he took much pleasure in leading the members into his old haunts and showing them unusual plants. Kate Furbish missed the next meeting, pleading an excess of company at home, and for the same reason missed the 1899 meeting in Aroostook County. Fernald was again the leader on that trip. He even rode in the train's engine cab (his brother was a railroad official) and persuaded the engineer to stop the train so that he could investigate an interesting bog at Crystal.

By 1900 Kate Furbish had some doubts about the society's survival. She disapproved of a plan to have the "Josses'" annual meeting merged with that of another scientific group, but she attended the meetings as often as her age and health permitted. Old-timers later recalled her astonishing endurance. Louise Coburn wrote:

I can see her as I saw her then, a little woman with uplifted head, already turned gray, in animated talk, or with bowed face using her keen eyes along a forest trail, or up a mountain path…. Her feet were as untiring as her eyes, and she could out-last many a younger woman on a cliff-side climb or river-bank scramble. Always obliging to tyros in the pursuit of botany, ready to name old floral friends on the minute, and to describe their habits and habitats, she was the most delightful of comrades on our Josselyn excursions.

Despite Kate's doubts, the Josselyn Society persisted, prospering from its mixture of enthusiastic amateurs and helpful professionals. One of the most memorable meetings for her was the one in 1902, which was held in Machias. She had always wanted to explore the state's easternmost coastline, and she planned a trip months ahead, hoping to proceed from Machias eastward to Lubec after the meeting. It happened that Fernald had arranged to botanize that summer around Cutler, a fishing village between Machias and Lubec, and suggested that Kate meet him there.

The excursion was a great success. The "Josses" stayed in an old hotel in Machias and were serenaded by a local band. Fernald came over from Cutler to lead several field trips. Kate, in turn, explored the shore at Cutler with him and then went on to Lubec, from which she sent him an unusual ragwort (*Senecio*) and reported: "I procured *Linaria vulgaris* [butter-and-eggs] this morn, on a high ledge on one of the high points running out into Quoddy Bay — there were at least fifty plants. I always associated it with old gardens…. the Bay is magnificent, pretty little Cutler seems very small now. It would seem that I might find something new here as it is only September 2."

Nearing seventy, Kate Furbish was becoming passionately interested in the plants of the Maine coast. This interest coincided with an inclination to spend less time in Brunswick and more in Wells, one of the haunts of her youth. She was finding fewer opportunities in Brunswick. Besides, most of her Brunswick relatives were scattered or long since dead, and her brother John was ill. It was only natural that she should spend more time in Wells.

Kate stayed in Wells with her cousin Joseph Donnell Eaton, who owned a farm, Eatoncroft, on Drake's Island. She would arrive by train at the Wells Beach Station, where Eaton picked her up in his "Sunday carriage" with its fine leather seat and drove her to the farm. It was located in an ideal setting for a botanist — a protected bay, low marshy areas, and a chain of eskers tucked around it. Eaton's daughter Louella was something of a naturalist herself and looked forward to following Kate on her wanderings into the marsh.

The area, in its topography and plant life, is more akin to southern New England than to the rocky coastline farther eastward, and Kate came upon a number of plants that are rare in Maine. In fact, several plants growing in York County are near the northern limits of their range, which made this area especially interesting to Merritt Fernald. Kate Furbish often wrote to him from Wells, reporting on what she was finding in the diked marsh. She sent him specimens of the slender blue flag, tried without success to find accommodations

GOOSEBERRY (Ribes cynosbati)
The fruit shown here belongs to the prickly gooseberry,
which is sometimes called dogberry.

PALE PURPLE CONEFLOWER (Echinacea pallida)
The painting was made life-size from a specimen Kate Furbish took from a hayfield in Wells.

SEASIDE GOLDENROD (Solidago sempervirens)
One of the twenty-seven goldenrods the artist painted in Maine, this was collected in Wells.

for him one spring on Drake's Island, and complained of the bitter cold there in early May.

"I came here all worked down — I have worked unmercifully this winter," she wrote. "Why I do not break, I do not know, I surely suffer enough physically. If I see a time while I am here when I can send for you to remain over Sunday I will write…. I've come to see what that 'Dyked Marsh' has to say for itself in May."

And yet, for Kate, there could be worse irritations than the cold. She spent the winter of 1902-1903 at Wells and wrote to Fernald:

WAXY CLYTOCYBE (Clytocybe lacasta)
The artist depicted the spores, as well as the stems in cross-section, of this mushroom she collected at Wells.

field and was the coauthor of a book on edible wild plants.) After leaving Wells in March 1903, Kate went to Boston, where the high points of her trip were visiting Fernald at the herbarium and attending a mycology lecture.

The subject of edible plants seems to have played a large role in her own lectures during that period. There still exists the draft of one such talk that she gave to the Norlands Grange near East Livermore, another of her favorite retreats from Brunswick. "You all know that I sing of the 'Wild Flowers,'" she told the audience, and went on to discuss their

"I am here for the winter, I cannot accomplish any good work at home. You will feel almost indignant for me when I tell you that I have been asked to make a large 'Crazy-Quilt' square of patchwork, and this request came from Brunswick; a part of the material was sent and I returned it with quite a sharp note. Some nonsense breaks my time when at home."

Kate had been embarked on a major project of her own for some time. Until 1897 the only nonflowering plants in which she had shown any interest were ferns, and those mainly because of her friendship with George Davenport. But in that year she began to collect mushrooms, and during the next eight seasons made 500 watercolors of these plants. What set her off in this direction is unclear. She undoubtedly came into contact with experts on fungi in the Josselyn Society and on visits to the Harvard Herbarium. It is possible also that she caught Fernald's enthusiasm for these and other edible wild plants. (Fernald was a tireless forager in the

useful and ornamental aspects. She pointed out the reliance of many European societies on collecting wild plants and advised Americans to emulate them, particularly in the pursuit of mushrooms.

"It has always been the accepted theory," she said, "that a 'Mushroom' is a plant which is not poisonous, and a 'Toadstool' a plant which is poisonous; or in other words, if it does *not* kill you it is a mushroom, and if it does kill you it is a toadstool."

Going further, she reminded her audience that the only way to be able to use and enjoy mushrooms, as with any other wild plants, was to learn to distinguish one species from another. Get to know the wild things, she urged. The man or woman who studies nature, who approaches it attentively, will find the world ever more beautiful and rewarding.

At one point she seemed to be expressing a hard-won, deeply personal truth. "A plant like an animal has its time of birth, its youth, its mature and its old age,

MUSHROOM (Strobilomyces strobilaceus)
One of the 500 or so mushrooms Kate Furbish painted around the turn of the century.
This species appears here still embedded in its original plot of Maine woods.

SLENDER BLUE FLAG (Iris prismatica)
*The marsh in Wells where Kate Furbish collected this specimen is the
only site where slender blue flag is now known to exist in Maine.*

134

and its natural *death*. It has its likes and its dislikes, its little fancies for sunlight or shade, its timid shrinking from cold. One of the most singular things about plants is the great differences in the length of their lives under the same conditions. Some live a few months, others three or four years, and still others twenty, forty, a hundred years or more."

Kate Furbish's religion and her study of the natural world had made her extremely conscious of the shape and progression of individual lives. There was "a time to be born, and a time to die," she believed with the author of Ecclesiastes, and lived in the light of that perception. "How fast life is ebbing out now!!!" she had exclaimed to Davenport as early as 1897. By then, she was dealing with people and things in the assurance of a harmonious conclusion to her days. It would have dismayed her to learn that she was to be tested by nearly thirty-five more years of life.

PAINTED TRILLIUM (Trillium undulatum)
*A member of the lily family, it was a favorite of Kate Furbish, who mentioned
other paintings of it that she had sent to friends and admirers.*

Flora of Maine

The Flora of Maine — the collection of paintings that was the lifework of Kate Furbish and included most of the flowering plants then known to grow within the state's boundaries — became an entity at last in the summer of 1908. Kate was in her seventy-fifth year. Change was all around her, the world in which she had worked was breaking up, and she believed she would soon be swept away with the rest. It was a matter of great anxiety to her that her Flora survive, not as a work of art, but as a useful reference for botanists who came after her. As a serious botanist, she wanted "to keep the stone rolling," as she had once written to George Davenport.

A sense of personal loss intensified her anxiety about her work. As the old century drew toward a close, her correspondence noted the deaths of Anne Jackson, her friend and fellow collector, and her brother Frank, who was unlucky to the end and died in Mexico City while trying to salvage another shaky business venture. "I am very down in the valley," she wrote to Davenport afterward, "have chills every afternoon. Something unusual for me, but my child brother's death is wearing me out."

Her brother John, the last of her immediate family and only two years younger than Kate, was the next to go, dying in 1905. That was, in fact, a year of last things for her. She made her final trip to Boston, Malden, and Cambridge, because after the death of an old friend with whom she had stayed, she no longer felt at home in the area. Her long correspondence with George Davenport was coming to an end. In June of that year, on what she described as "a botanical afternoon," she wrote to him, asking about some ferns he had collected in Maine and assuring him that the ferns he had given her for her own collection remained in excellent condition. She concluded: "I always think of you with gratitude for the benefit which you have been to me and I hope to see you again in life. We do not feel as much courage now-a-days, do we?"

Apparently they never saw each other again. Davenport died two years later. Though he did not finish his manual of the North American ferns, Kate must have taken comfort from the obituary written by one of his colleagues, J. S. Collins, for *Rhodora*:

The last two years his time was largely spent in his garden; here in small compass was a remarkable variety of conditions, rich ground, swamp, rocky hillside; here he had growing nearly every fern found in New England, and here too he watched with much interest

PURPLE CLEMATIS (Clematis verticillaris)
This rather scarce vine was brought by a Mr. Silas Niles to Kate Furbish from the Fish River when she
was working in Aroostook County. She was able to keep in mind the proportions and
angles of intersection among the various parts of the living plant.

138

PUSSYTOES (Antennaria plantaginifolia and A. neglecta)
*The former, on the left has the broad plantainlike leaves, while the field
pussytoes, the more common species, is on the right.*

*a little group of flowering plants, selected as best show-
ing the phenomena of heredity and mutation that now
attract so much interest. The enthusiasm with which he
showed me these treasures one Sunday morning early
last October will always be a most pleasant recollec-
tion.*

One solid support remained in Kate Furbish's life.

Merritt Fernald, growing steadily in the estimation of
other professional botanists, was as attentive to her as
ever. A man of compact build, with a neat, pointed
beard, he remained adventurous in his botanizing and
conservative in private life. He never learned to drive a
car, and he kept his students segregated by sex both in
the laboratory and on field trips. He had married in

1907, but when Kate called on him for assistance the next year, he came. She was now in a rush to settle her affairs in a proper way.

She was about to bring two major projects to completion, for besides the Flora there was her large collection of plant specimens, amounting to some 4,000 herbarium sheets, which she had decided to send to Cambridge. A thorny problem in respect to the sheets was that the plants had been collected over a span of nearly 40 years, and many of the scientific names by which they were labeled had become obsolete. The chore of going through them to check the names for accuracy was beyond her at that point, and she needed assistance. No one in America was more qualified for this task than Fernald.

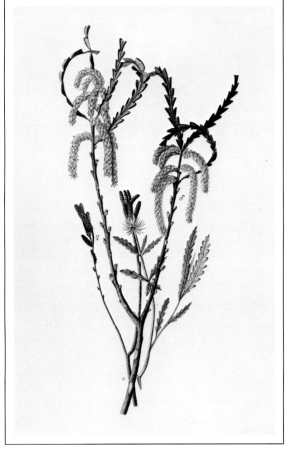

SWEET FERN (*Comptonia peregrina*)
The staminate and pistillate parts often grow on the same plant,
as they do here. A full botanical study.

Fernald disposed of the formidable task of checking the Furbish collection and was soon off on a field trip. Kate then turned to packing the sheets for shipment to the Harvard Herbarium, where they became part of the huge collection of the New England Botanical Club, which is housed there. To help her with the packing, she hired Emory Booker, a Brunswick boy, who recalled in later years, "While we were loading the crates, Miss Furbish could not be interrupted and told me to turn all callers away." Fernald helped Kate also to put the finishing touches on her Flora. For some years she had applied herself at intervals to mounting her paintings on heavy paper and affixing labels, marked "Flora of Maine" with her name below, to the paintings themselves. Apparently

Fernald went to Brunswick for three days during the summer of 1908 to help Kate put her botanical sheets in order. He took with him the seventh edition of Gray's *New Manual of Botany*, published that year and edited by B. L. Robinson of Harvard University and himself; he inscribed a copy to "Miss Furbish with affectionate greetings." In their introduction to the new edition, Robinson and Fernald noted that there had been extensive nomenclatural changes in the wake of the International Botanical Congress held in Vienna in 1905. The scientific names of many plants in the old manual and various field guides (as well as on Kate's herbarium sheets) were obsolete.

she was not bothered by the fact that some of the labels encroached on the fringes of her compositions, for the labels contained pertinent information and thus reflected her utilitarian view of the collection. Because there was a botanical sheet for each painting, she had simply revised the labels whenever necessary to conform with new nomenclature.

Kate had decided to present the Flora of Maine to Bowdoin College. The Flora consists of 1,326 watercolors and sketches assembled in 14 volumes, each measuring 20 inches by 16½ inches, and bound in half-Morocco leather with gold tooling and marbled endpapers. Each volume bears on its spine the names of

HEPATICA (Hepatica americana)
In the Furbish collection there are four studies of Hepatica — a double-flowered,
a pink phase, a blue phase, and the white one shown here.

Kate Furbish at seventy-four poses on the back steps of her Lincoln Street home,
severely gowned and ornately hatted, alongside the homely pump.

the plant families (*Ranunculaceae, Cruciferae*, and so forth) that it contains. She decided to present, also, two volumes holding her paintings of mushrooms, and some miscellaneous unbound flower paintings.

Bowdoin accepted the Flora with enthusiasm. Its president, William DeWitt Hyde, wrote to Kate expressing the college's gratitude and, in an effort to gather more information on the acquisition, asked her to elaborate on three questions — the nature of the collection, the amount of time and labor that brought it to completion, and the way in which she worked. Replying from East Livermore, where she was staying in the spring of 1909, she answered the first two questions succinctly. She had collected and sketched the plants between April 1870, and October 1908. The *amount* of time involved, however, could not be determined, even if the artist had been "a wage earner."

She took more time with the third question, neglecting any description of technique or materials, but setting down the few sentences that have been quoted more often than anything else she ever wrote and form the basis of her popular image. There is no doubt that this is how she wanted to be seen, another instance of her ability to dramatize herself.

142

ARROW ARUM (Peltandra virginica)
*Kate Furbish wrote, "I procured this plant in a bog corner of
Pleasant and Spring Street, now filled in," in Brunswick.*

It has been accomplished by means of hard work and persistent effort, and without regard to fatigue. I have wandered alone for the most part, on the highways and in the hedges, on foot, in hayricks, in country mail-stages (often in Aroostook County, with a revolver on the seat), on improvised rafts (equipped with hammer, saw, nails, knife, rubber-boots, vasculum, etc.), in rowboats, on logs, crawling on hands and knees on the surface of bogs, and backing out, when I dared not walk, in order to procure a coveted treasure. Called 'crazy,' a 'fool,' and this is the way that my work has been done. The Flowers being my only society, and the Manuals the only literature for months together. Happy, happy hours!

143

The college provided a fitting receptacle for the Flora — a large cabinet of quartersawed oak, with drawers lined with felt to hold each volume, and a glass top for display. This gesture by Bowdoin touched Kate, and she expressed her gratitude to President Hyde. "It is indeed 'a beauty' as you said in your note," she told him. "I have laid all but one of my children to rest on its velvet couches, taking that with me for company and instruction."

Kate's letter to the president bore almost immediate fruit, for direct quotations from it about her adventurous life appeared in the next "Report of the President" in the *Bowdoin College Bulletin*, taking precedence over plans for a new gymnasium.

What of the paintings themselves? No formal assessment has been attempted of the drawings and watercolors that Kate Furbish made during the forty years in the field, in her second-floor bedroom/studio in the little house on Lincoln Street, and in the homes away from home that she frequented.

It is known that she had admirers among her contemporaries. Davenport liked her paintings, and even mentioned her blue gentian in a poem he once published. Other botanists asked her to make paintings for them. Fernald admired her work from the time he was a boy. Since her death, botanists and lovers of wild flowers have turned to the Furbish paintings in their research and found them accurate and satisfying.

That judgment, she would have thought, was the

PENNYROYAL (Hedeoma pulegioides)
The floral composition here, with its intertwined parts, is more elaborate than that in most of the artist's strictly "botanical" portraits.

highest compliment that could be paid to her work. Before 1870 and occasionally thereafter, she painted for her own pleasure or to present decorative watercolors to friends. But, in the Flora of Maine, science rather than aesthetics was the chief aim. She referred to herself as a "botanic-artist" and played down the pleasure principle in her work by remarking that painting plants that were not attractive could often be tedious.

"I do not claim Artistic merit," she told President Hyde of Bowdoin, "but merely a truthful representation of what I saw in the plants, free from all decorative effects. As such I hope that they [the paintings] will assist the earnest student instead of serving merely to entertain the visitor."

In the sense that she did not attempt to impose her will on the paper, Kate Furbish was not an artist. She had spent her life observing the natural world, and thus had a special ability to interpret a plant in the manner of the scientist. Above all, she strove for accuracy. She recognized what she did *not* want her paintings to be. Beginning in the sixteenth century, for instance, the quality of woodcuts in the herbals on which botanists had depended for so long began to decline. Artists had simply copied and recopied the early woodcuts, corrupting the basic structure of plants as an ancient text might be corrupted after centuries of successive copiers, so that the plants illustrated could no longer be recognized as distinct species.

Equally unsatisfactory to Kate Furbish was that

WILD ROSE (Rosa sp.)

The painting contains all the stages we associate with wild roses — the fully opened flower with its crowded circle of stamens, buds both closed and partly opened, leaves and thorns, and ripening as well as fully developed fruit, or hips.

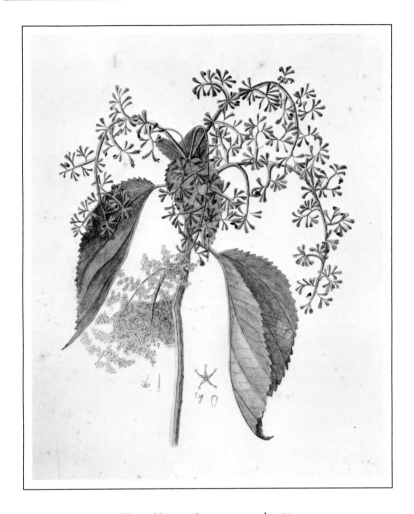

WOOD NETTLE (Laportea canadensis)
*Kate Furbish made a sympathetic drawing of a plant whose stinging
hairs can be especially irritating to both hikers and botanists.*

much decorative painting in her own time (which has been called "the age of flowers" because of the abundance of its ornamental floral themes) pictured botanical features (fruit, thorns, and so forth) more as rhythmic, patternistic figures than as functioning parts of plants. Blossoms appeared as mere blobs of color, or "paper staining," as one critic put it. Stamens and pistils appeared as blurred impressions. As Kate Furbish wrote to President Hyde, "You know that an artist need not count his stamens and pistils."

No element was slurred in her own work. She was careful to set down on paper what another critic has called "the structural miracle of cell and tissue." She often followed the tradition of the old herbalists and illustrated the complete plant, including the root system. She wanted first of all to establish the nature of the species and to show its structure, its unique way of growth, and the number and position of the stamens and pistils. Every function had to be comprehended before the drawing was begun; the plant had to be understood from the inside out. She wanted the viewer to see the blossom, not just as an intricate design, but as a functioning organ that attracts insects and leads them to its innermost recesses as a part of the pollination process. She wanted the viewer to see leaves, not just as a swirl of ornate patterns, but as functioning parts of a vascular system. She drew the entire plant as a living organism.

Yet, amazingly, there is no awkward composition in the entire collection. She calculated the space available to her on each sheet, even when she began with an incomplete plant. It is seldom possible to have all elements of a plant — buds, mature flowers, fruit, and fresh green leaves — available at once, and thus provision had to be made in the composition for later additions. She was able to complete the compositions while keeping in mind the proportions and angles of intersection among the various parts of the living plant.

The use of a hand lens and sometimes a camera lucida (for tracing the shapes of tiny seeds onto paper) must have played an important part in Kate Furbish's work. Even the smallest variation can be seen in most of her paintings, including the minute hairs and spines that are important points for the botanist-student because the division of species may depend on such matters. Her original paintings remain valuable to students because, like the original plants themselves, they reveal more of their minute details under a lens.

Part of the secret of her success as a botanist-artist lay in the exceptional coordination of eye and hand. Many contemporaries commented on the penetration of her gaze. "She had the sort of eyes that are made for seeing," her friend Louise Coburn wrote, "and nothing escaped the swift circle of her glance." In old photographs her eyes stand out as her most impressive feature. The steadiness of her gaze was refined by long concentration in the field, swiftly and accurately recording the images that were transmitted to her hand. Speed, in fact, was an adjunct of accuracy on many occasions when, after an arduous day in the field, she pushed herself to capture the posture or color of a fast-wilting plant. Such conditions demanded of Kate considerable skill in selecting and mixing the correct colors with exactly the right amounts of water to provide the opacity, and thus the degree of solidity, that she wanted to impart.

Despite Kate Furbish's avowed utilitarian purpose, her Flora emerged as more than a field guide or a tool for botany students. Like a good portrait painter who carefully studies the shape of the head or the characteristic attitudes of the subject, she captured the *character* of each plant. Being familiar with hundreds of specimens of each species, she was able to depict the natural way in which each plant sprang from the soil and assumed its place in its proper habitat.

And so, for the viewer, there is a reflective pleasure in observing the harmonious ordering of the parts of her plants, and in apprehending the function of each and seeing how they relate to one another. In her haste to capture a fleeting tone in a leaf or a stem, she sometimes painted in only a small part of the plant as a guide for the day when she could return to it in leisure. Thus, a number of her portraits remained chiefly sketches. But the finished paintings are as remarkable for their authentic color as for the plants' structure and posture. Seen at leisure under artificial light in Bowdoin's Hawthorne-Longfellow Library, the paintings evoke the experiences and perceptions of a lone woman exploring nature a century ago. Despite her dogged utilitarian approach, Kate Furbish still gives aesthetic pleasure to those who study her work.

In 1911 the Josselyn Botanical Society held its annual summer meeting in Brunswick. The members explored meadows along the Androscoggin River in Brunswick and Topsham and found rare plants in the marshes at Bath, expeditions on which Kate Furbish, as one of the members recalled, "acted as pilot." An afternoon was set aside for the members and their guests to visit the Bowdoin College Library and examine the Flora of Maine. And that evening the "Josses" elected the "botanic-artist" as the president of their society for the year 1911–1912.

NORTHERN WHITE VIOLET (Viola pallens)
This species, with fragrant flowers, is still found throughout Maine in those wet places loved by Kate Furbish.

The Last Decades

Beginning in 1916 Kate Furbish appended to each of her letters, just beneath her signature, the year of her birth and the present year: "1834 - 1916." It gave her correspondence something of the aspect of a tombstone at first, but as one year succeeded another and the second date changed accordingly, it began to seem almost an act of bravado. How taut could she stretch this line of life?

All surviving letters from these last years (thanks to the care of the Gray Herbarium) were written to the man who now assumed all-encompassing significance for her. Merritt Fernald continued to be her strongest link to the world outside Brunswick and even to her own strenuous past. (She sometimes signed herself "Your lifelong friend, Kate Furbish.") She continued collecting plants, more and more the "dooryard and garden weeds," and regularly sent off packages of dried specimens to Fernald at the Gray Herbarium. People from Brunswick and the nearby countryside brought her plants to identify. Neighbors stopped to see her, and some of the newer colleges in northern New England asked her to contribute to their herbaria. But her correspondence with Fernald, and an occasional visit from him, were the bright spots in every year. On the other hand, a mix-up

or change of plans that prevented his visit could bring her to tears. We catch glimpses of her life through those letters:

Brunswick, September 15, 1916 — Why I need as much discipline in my last days I do not know: but it has come thick and fast of late, and this disappointment [she had been out when Fernald called at her house] is the hardest of all to bear, and will last me longest, unless I see you sooner than I think I shall.... I passed two weeks at Casco, 26 miles N.W. of Portland. It is composed of hills (300 ft.) very steep, and at their feet lovely ponds.... The White Closed Gentian was very attractive. It was very abundant in a bog, which was "up to the top of rubber boots," with a deal of suction.

Brunswick, April 29, 1917 — It is hard for me to realize that the little fellow whom I first met in '80 is now the distinguished man whom I am addressing on the same subject which engaged his thoughts at that early age. But you are too busy to look backward.... Please give my kind regards to my friends at the Herbarium.

Moseley Farm, Freeport, January 3, 1919 — I was unable to get the plants off to you before I left home. I could not get myself off. I was brought here in a closed carriage. I have been engaged for some time past in

MEADOWSWEET (Spiraea latifolia)
The genus name, meaning wreath, refers to the abundance of tiny flowers.
A familiar plant for Kate Furbish from childhood through old age.

DANDELION (Taraxacum officinale)
Among the plants that Kate Furbish could continue to observe at Grant's Hospital in
her old age. This specimen, taken from cultivated ground in Brunswick,
was a "full, healthy nourished plant," as we can see.

translating a French work entitled *La Cathédrale* for our weekday Bible class, and I find it very pleasurable. *"Employment, employment, o, that is enjoyment!"*

Brunswick, June 19, 1920 — I am tottering to my end as fast as my great constitution will permit.... I never saw the "wild flowers" more robust than they are this Spring, and such an abundance of them! ...my eyes are still clear and I shall insist upon hard work — as long as it is possible to make the feet and eyes do my bidding, pain or no pain.

Grant's Hospital, Brunswick, April 4, 1921 — I came [here] in November, and instead of employing a Nurse at Home ...I said to myself if I remain at Home I shall do nothing but use my waning strength in Home-keeping; but if I go to a Hospital where I have no friends, I shall not only be alone but have a

COMMON PLANTAIN (Plantago major)
A low plant with minute greenish-white flowers, it was one of the
"weeds" Kate Furbish continued to find after she became
confined to her house and dooryard.

"trained" Nurse to look after me ...this is just the season to be here as the plants with all their fascinations are near at hand as you will probably see in company with this Note. The grasses I do not study.

Grant's Hospital, Brunswick, July 13, 1921 — The Josselyn Botanical Society is in Brunswick this week. Miss Coburn, Willis, and a younger woman whose name I did not catch came out to see me yesterday afternoon. I think that my Nephew [Benjamin Furbish, who became the treasurer of Bowdoin College] may have Expressed a box full of dried plants to the Herbar-ium 'ere this; which represents the Brunswick plants I have collected the past two Summers. I only send them for locality; though I think there may be a few desirable specimens. Charlotte Cushman left the Stage three times before her final "Good-bye." I am in the same position; I love my work too well to leave it.

Grant's Hospital, Brunswick, May 1923 — What fine work you accomplished last Season — I judge from all I have read in Rhodora.... During the Winter months I passed much of the time in bed.... I often ask myself what I accomplished, and if I am really as well

152

as I should have been had I gone to Florida. I dislike travelling so very much ...and the older we grow where there is no mental decline the real life seems more and more desirable. I for one esteem it. I think of it all as only a part of Eternity.

This was the last letter to Fernald that has been preserved. There is a later glimpse of Kate in her nineties, recorded in the *Appreciation* by Louise Coburn, who was one of the first woman graduates of Colby College and a Josselyn Society member. The brief, undated publication contained what were probably the first reproductions (in black and white) of Furbish paintings, including the pitcher plant, fringed gentian, mountain laurel, and common clematis.

"When I last called on her not many weeks ago her hair was snow-white," Louise Coburn wrote, "but her interest in Botany seemed to be as lively as ever, and her room was littered with piles of dried plants. She told me she could walk by herself over the farm [probably the farm of C. C. Moseley in Freeport] where she was staying, in search of her specimens, and turning the leaves of Gray's *Manual* to verify a description she read the fine print without glasses."

Kate Furbish died of heart failure in Brunswick on December 6, 1931. She was ninety-seven years old. Three days later funeral services were held for her in Saint Paul's Episcopal Church, whose liturgy she had so much admired in a letter to her cousin Pamela seventy years before. Three of her beloved Furbishes, her nephews Benjamin, Samuel, and J. Arthur, acted as her pallbearers, and she was buried nearby at Pine Grove Cemetery.

Her very long life had come to a close. But the image, the identity so arduously won as artist and botanist, survives.

The Garden of Maine
Indicated here are the principal localities targeted by Kate Furbish during her long campaign to collect and paint the state's flowering plants.

QUEBEC

Quebec

St. Lawrence River

CANADA
UNITED STATES

St. John River

Fort Kent

Van Buren

Caribou

Aroostook River

Fort Fairfield

NEW BRUNSWICK

St. John River

Patten

Mt. Katahdin

Penobscot River

Passamaquoddy Bay

NEW HAMPSHIRE

Kennebec River

Androscoggin

Farmington

Chesterville

East Livermore

Fayette Ridge

Norlands Grange

Augusta

Poland Springs

Merrymeeting Bay

Bangor Bog

Orono

Bangor

Machias

Lubec
Cutler

Machias Bay

Brunswick
Freeport
(Mosley Farm)

Portland

Casco Bay

Harpswell

Penobscot Bay

GULF OF MAINE

Wells

Map by Jan Crosen

Bibliography

As noted in the Preface and Acknowledgments, this book is based in large part on primary sources not yet published; those materials include journals, correspondence, and memorabilia in the possession of Kate Furbish's descendants, Special Collections in the Hawthorne-Longfellow Library at Bowdoin College, and the files of the Gray Herbarium at Harvard. Following is a list of published materials also relied on, keyed to individual chapters.

Chapter One: Much of the background for the Brunswick region in the nineteenth century is found in *History of Brunswick, Topsham and Harpswell, Maine*, by George Augustus Wheeler, M.D., and Henry Warren Wheeler (Boston, 1878). Also see "Facts About Brunswick, Maine," by John Furbish, a handwritten chronicle of life in Brunswick during the 1860s and 1870s and reproduced in a facsimile edition by the Pejepscot Historical Society of Brunswick in 1976.

Chapter Three: Besides Josselyn's narratives, see *A Story of North American Botany*, by Andrew Denny Rodgers III (Princeton, 1942), and *Asa Gray*, by A. Hunter Dupree (Cambridge, 1959). A lively account of some aspects of early American botany can be found in *A Species of Eternity*, by Joseph Kastner (New York, 1977). See also the following articles: "Dr. Aaron Young, Jr., and the Botanical Survey of Maine," by A. H. Norton in *Rhodora* (1935, Vol. 37: pp. 1-16), and "Further Light on Aaron Young, Jr.'s *Flora of Maine*," by Ralph C. Bean in *Rhodora* (1953, Vol. 55: pp. 293-296). Gawler's remarks on Joseph Blake and the excerpt from Blake's original report on the star saxifrage appear in *Rare Vascular Plants of Maine*, prepared for the state's Critical Areas Program in 1981 by L. M. Eastman and Susan C. Gawler; this volume is itself a gold mine of information on Maine botany.

Chapter Four: The letter from Kate Furbish to Mrs. Henry Johnson was uncovered by Polly Greason while we were working on this book. The remarks of Charlotte Coues on spring flowers was quoted in *Elliott Coues: Naturalist and Frontier Historian*, by P. R. Cutright and M. J. Brodhead (Urbana, 1981, p. 20). See also *How to Know the Wild Flowers*, by Mrs. William Starr Dana (New York, 1893), and *The Heritage of Our Maine Wildflowers*, by Judith B. Johnson (Rockland, Maine, 1978).

Chapter Five: The reference to a shortage of males in post-Civil War New England is from *Alice James, A Biography*, by Jean Strouse (Boston, 1980).

Chapter Six: The correspondence between Kate Furbish and George Davenport, as well as background on Davenport, is in the Gray Herbarium.

Chapter Seven: There is an extensive treatment of Furbish's lousewort, with bibliography, in *Furbish's Lousewort in Maine*, prepared for the Maine Critical Areas Program by Susan C. Gawler in 1983. Kate Furbish's article, "A Botanist's Trip to the 'Aroostook,'" appeared in two parts in *American Naturalist* (June 1881, pp. 469-470, and May 1882, pp. 397-399).

Chapter Eight: There is a copy of Kate Furbish's Portland address in the files of the Gray Herbarium.

Chapters Nine, Ten, and Eleven: There is a wealth of material on Merritt Fernald and the early "Josses" in *Bulletin of the Josselyn Botanical Society of Maine* (No. 10, 1975). Dr. Eugene Ogden, a Josselyn member, and Emory Booker of Brunswick also supplied helpful anecdotes and background material.

Chapter Twelve: For a far-ranging survey, see *The Art of Botanical Illustration*, by Wilfrid Blunt (London, 1950).

Chapter Thirteen: See "Kate Furbish, Botanist," an Appreciation by Louise H. Coburn (no date) in the collection of the Hawthorne-Longfellow Library at Bowdoin College.

Index

An Appreciation

For many decades now, lovers of wildflowers and Maine's various natural landscapes,
scientists tracing the original distribution of native plants, and painters interested
in the art of botanical illustration have been drawn to the collection of Kate
Furbish's watercolors at Bowdoin College. These visitors invariably pass on
to friends and colleagues their admiration for the poetic nature of the
vision set down more than a century earlier by a singular woman.
Thus has grown a special community of appreciation.

One such visitor to the Furbish Collection several years ago was Judith Falk of
Washington, D.C. An amateur watercolorist and part-time resident of Maine,
she is more than commonly open to the world of form and color on display
in the big folios preserved at Bowdoin. Now, because of her commitment
to that century-old vision, and by means of a very generous gift, Judith
Falk has made it possible for many of the paintings to be reproduced
here for a much wider audience than Kate Furbish ever dreamed of.
That community of appreciation keeps on growing.